Once Upon a Time in Japan

装幀 ● 菊地信義
装画 ● 愛企画センター

Published by Kodansha International Ltd.,
17-14, Otowa 1-chome, Bunkyo-ku, Tokyo 112-8652.

First Edition 1997

99 10 9 8 7
ISBN4-7700-2173-9

まんが日本昔ばなし
Once Upon a Time in Japan

川内彩友美［編］
ラルフ・マッカーシー［訳］

Bilingual Books

はじめに

りくつもなにもいらない、見終わったときに、胸の中を暖かいものが過ぎれば……。そんな素朴な願いからはじまり、すでに二十年あまりを経過した「まんが日本昔ばなし」のTVシリーズの代表作をバイリンガルでお届けいたします。

遠い昔から、日本の母から子へと語り継がれてきた昔ばなし──、ここには、日本の母の愛と精神が、豊かで美しい華となって輝いています。

「昔ばなし」という言葉は、民俗学者の柳田國男（1875-1962）が考案したもので、それまで口碑、民譚、童話などとさまざまに呼ばれていた表現を一つにしたものです。

一般に、虚構や空想にもとづく物語性に富んだはなしを「昔ばなし」と称しています。これに対して、事実と信じられている過去の出来事を伝えているのが「伝説」です。

昔ばなしも伝説も、もともとは「語り」によって伝えられてきたものですが、伝説は、その事実が起こった場所や時間、それに関わった人物などの名称が明確に伝えられるのにくらべて、昔ばなしは、「むかしむかし、あるところに……」といった不特定の時、場所をあらわす言葉ではじまり、最後は「……であったとさ」という、はなしの内容は伝え聞いたものであることを示す表現でおわるのが特徴です。

PREFACE

Sometimes you just want to forget theories and logic and watch something that leaves you feeling warm inside. This simple wish of mine led to twenty years of the television series *Manga Nippon Mukashi-banashi*, the best episodes of which we now present in this bilingual format.

These tales are the fruits of maternal love, passed from mothers to children in Japan since time immemorial. The term *mukashi-banashi*, or "tales of old," was coined by the ethnologist Kunio Yanagita (1875–1962) to describe what had previously been known by various other names: *kohi* (oral tradition), *mindan* (folktales), and *dowa* (children's stories).

Mukashi-banashi are usually richly layered stories based on fictional characters and events. Historical tales, commonly believed to be grounded in fact, are known as *densetsu*, or legends.

Both *mukashi-banashi* and *densetsu* are part of an oral tradition handed down through the ages. But whereas *densetsu* clearly identify the time, setting, and characters involved in the events they describe, *mukashi-banashi* typically begin with a vague "*Mukashi mukashi, aru tokoro ni*" ("Long, long ago, in a certain place") and end with *de atta to sa*" (roughly, "or so they say"), indicating that the story has been passed from teller to teller.

そして登場人物には、おじいさん、おばあさん、太郎や次郎などといった、どこにでもいそうな人物の名称が使われます。

　この本に収録したおはなしは、いずれも日本人になじみの深いものばかりですが、日本の昔ばなしは代表的なものだけでも、ゆうに三百はあります。それらにはどんな寓意（ぐうい）が隠されているのか、それを探っていくことは大きな楽しみの一つです。

　また日本の昔ばなしのなかには中国や韓国、さらになぜか欧米の昔ばなしと似たものも少なくありません。その謎を探るのも、たいそう興味深いことでしょう。

　とはいえ私は、まず何よりもりくつぬきにおはなしを楽しみ、あじわってほしいのです。文化の違いのある世界の人たちに向けて、「かぐや姫」などでは内容的に理解しづらい部分を英文では補足しました。ぜひ、この英訳を参考に、あなた自身のことばで、世界の子供たちに暖かく語ってあげてください。

　古くから伝えられてきた日本の昔ばなしが大人から子供たちへと語り継がれるとき、ほのぼのとした愛の灯（ひ）が、大きな手から小さな手へとわたされてゆきます。そのなかから、人間としてのたいせつな思いやりや、真心が育（はぐく）まれてゆき、いつまでも愛と精神の華として、美しく咲きつづけてほしい、そう私は希（ねが）っております。

川内彩友美

The characters populating these tales of old are often the familiar archetypes common to fairy tales: the ubiquitous *ojiisan to obaasan* (old man and old woman), or men with names like Taro or Jiro.

The tales included in this book are all close to the hearts of the Japanese, but there are at least three hundred *mukashi-banashi* that could be considered standards of Japanese folklore. Picking out the morals of these stories is part of the pleasure of reading them.

Some are similar to Chinese and Korean folktales, and there are curious resemblances to Western fairy tales as well. Unraveling these connections would be a fascinating pursuit.

But my wish is that readers from many countries will enjoy these stories with the heart rather than the mind. In order to make the story more widely accessible, there has been a certain amount of aug-mentation and adaptation, particularly in the case of *The Bamboo-Cutter's Tale*. I hope this English trans-lation will help grown-ups recount our *mukashi-banashi* to the children of the world.

These tales are lights of love, passed from big hands to smaller ones since time out of mind. May they continue to nurture humanity and compassion, linking adults and children through the ages to come.

Sayumi Kawauchi

まんが
日本昔ばなし

Once Upon a Time
in Japan

目次

CONTENTS

一寸法師

　　むかしむかし、そのむかし、都から遠くはなれた
いなかに、一人の男の子がうまれた。

　ところが、どういうわけか、この男の子は、背の丈が
おとなの小指ほどしかなかった。

　それでも両親は、天からのさずかりものじゃからと、
おおいによろこび、「一寸法師」と名づけて、たーんとか
わいがったそうな。

　ところが、一寸法師は、どういうわけか、何年たって
もちーっとも大きくならなかった。いつまでたっても小
指ほどの大きさしかなかったそうな。

　でも、一寸法師は元気だった。元気のよさでは、どの
子どもたちにも負けなかった。

Issun Boshi, the Inch-High Samurai

Long, long ago in a village far from the capital, a baby boy was born. Now there was nothing unusual about that, except that this child was no bigger than your little finger. His parents didn't care how tiny he was, though. They were delighted to be blessed with such a beautiful son, and they showered him with love. They named him "Issun Boshi," which means "Inch-High Priestling."

Issun Boshi never did get very much taller. Even after several years had passed, he was still about as big as your little finger. It certainly wasn't that he didn't eat enough—his appetite was

ごはんもたくさん食べた。

こうして法師は、からだこそ小さかったが、すくすくと元気にそだっていった。

そんなある日のこと。一寸法師は、高い木の上にのぼった。

「わあ、すげえや。よく見えるなあ。」

一寸法師の目の前には、うまれてはじめて見る、広い広い景色があった。

川はどこまでもどこまでも遠くまで流れていた。

そして、その夜――。

「おとう、川はどこまでつづいとるんじゃあ。」

「どこまでって、山のむこうじゃよ。」

「山のむこうにはなにがあるだ?」

「なにがって、京の都じゃよ。都にはな、そりゃもう、たくさんの人がおってなあ。それに、大きな寺ややしきがあってのう。それはにぎやかなところじゃ。」

「ふーん。」

法師の都へのゆめは、ぐんぐんとふくらんだ。

「よし、おらー、都へいくだ!」

「な、なんじゃと?」

「都へいって、おさむらいになるだ。」

the same as any normal, healthy boy's. And he was cheerful, full of energy, and very strong for his size.

One day while Issun Boshi was playing outside, he climbed to the top of a tall tree. "Wow!" he cried. "What a big world it is!" He could see a great river winding and winding away into the distance.

That night, Issun Boshi asked his father, "Pa, where does that river flow to?"

"Why, to the other side of the mountains, son."

"What's on the other side of the mountains?"

"Well, that's where the capital, Kyoto, is. And in the capital, there are lots and lots of people. And big temples and mansions, and estates where the samurai warriors live … Oh, it's a very exciting place."

"Gosh!"

From that moment on, Hoshi, as his parents called him, could think of nothing but the capital. One day he went to his parents and told them he'd made a decision.

"I'm going to the capital."

"You—you're what?"

"I'm going to the capital to become a samurai."

　両親はひっしでとめたが、法師の決心はかたかった。

　とうとう両親は、法師のために麦わらのさやに針の刀、そしておわんの舟にはしのかいを用意したのだった。

「おとう、おっかあ、たっしゃでな。」

　おわんの舟にのって、法師がいよいよ出発するときがきた。

「おめえも、のう。」

「からだに気をつけてなあ。」

　年とった両親をのこして、法師は都へむかってこぎだした。

「さようならあ〜。」

　故郷の景色にわかれをつけながら、法師は小川をどんどん、どんどん流れていった。

　おわんの舟は、岩にぶつかり、滝を下り、何度も危険をくぐりぬけ、やっとこさ、大川へとこぎだした。

　とちゅう、あらしにもあった。

　でも、一寸法師は負けなかった。小さなからだに大きなのぞみ。一寸法師の見るゆめは、いつも大きくふくらんだ。

His mother and father tried desperately to make him change his mind, but in vain. At last, seeing how determined he was, they gave in. His father found a needle and straw to serve as a sword and scabbard, and his mother gave him a rice bowl to use as a boat and a chopstick to paddle it with. The next day they all walked to the river.

"Pa ... Ma ... Take care of yourselves."

"You too, son."

"Be careful, Hoshi."

The inch-high youngster began paddling downstream toward the capital.

"Goodbye!" Hoshi took a fond last look at his old hometown as the swift current of the river carried him off. Along the way, his rice-bowl boat slammed into rocks, dropped over waterfalls, bounced through rapids, and was tossed about in raging storms. But Issun Boshi never gave up. Tiny as he was, his dream only grew bigger, his ambition greater, as he overcame each new peril.

19

そして、故郷をでてから何十日めか。

「あっ、都だ、都へついたぞーっ。」

大川のむこうに、都が見えて

きた。いままでのつかれもなん

のその、一寸法師はもうれつな

いきおいで舟をこいだ。

都は、法師が想像していた

よりも、ずっとずっと大きか

った。りっぱだった。

そして法師は、そのなかでもとくにりっぱなやしきの

前で足をとめた。

「よしっ、このやしきにきめたぞ。」

そのやしきは、三条の大臣というお武家さまのやしき

だった。

大臣は、法師のからだがあまりにも小さいのでびっく

りされたが、小さなからだにあわず、元気でやる気満々

なのを見こんで、「おもしろいやつじゃ。」と、やしきに

つかえることをゆるされた。

法師は、大臣のひとり娘、春姫さまの家来としておつ

かえすることになった。

「法師、よろしくね。」

こうして一寸法師は、

うつくしい春姫さまの

もとで、本を読み、書

をならい、琴やつづみ

Many weeks went by before Hoshi at last caught sight of his destination. "The capital! There's the capital! I made it!" Tired as he was, Issun Boshi paddled for all he was worth.

The capital was even larger and more beautiful than he had imagined. There were more grand estates than you could count, and Hoshi stopped before the grandest of them all. "This is the place for me," he declared, knocking on the gate.

The estate belonged to the famous samurai, Lord Sanjo. When Hoshi was brought before him, the great man was astounded to see how tiny his visitor was. But he could tell that the little fellow was full of spirit.

"Enterprising chap, aren't you?" said Lord Sanjo after he'd heard Hoshi's story. "All right, why don't you stay here and serve me? I'm sure we can find a place for you."

Hoshi was given a job as guard and playmate to Lord Sanjo's only daughter, Haruhime. Soon he and the lovely maiden became the best of friends. Together they read books, practiced writing, and played music—Hoshi beating a tiny

のおてつだい。そして、剣の修行にはげんだ。

りっぱなさむらいになるために。

大きなのぞみをはたすために。

そして、またたくまに何年かがすぎていった。

都はいま、花ざかりの春。

ある日、春姫さまは清水寺へおまいりすることになった。

そのころ、都にはらんぼうな鬼があらわれ、若くうつくしい娘たちをさらうといううわさだった。

そこで、春姫さまが鬼にさらわれてはいけないと、大臣は強そうな家来をえらんで、おともにつけた。

「わたしもまいります。」

一寸法師も名のりでて、ついていくことになった。

そして、ぶじに清水寺のおまいりをすませてからの帰り道、春姫さまの行列が、とある山道にさしかかったときだった。

と、ついにでました、赤鬼一ぴき。

「きゃあーっ。」

「で、でたあっ！」

hand drum while Haruhime plucked at her koto.

Issun Boshi also trained every day at swords-manship. His heart was still set on becoming a great samurai. And while he passed his time in this way, chasing his dream, the years went quickly by....

It was spring in the capital—the most beauti-ful season. One day when the cherry trees were all in full bloom, Haruhime decided to visit Kiyomizu Temple to worship beneath the famous blossoms there.

Now, at that time there were rumors of hideous demons who would come out at night and kidnap lovely young girls. To guard against this, Lord Sanjo selected seven of his strongest warriors to accompany Haruhime on her visit to the temple. Issun Boshi also volunteered to go along.

They arrived at Kiyomizu Temple safely. It was after praying there, as they walked home on the dark, winding mountain road, that a ferocious demon suddenly stepped out of the brush in front of them.

"Eeek!" The women in the group fell trembling to the ground.

女たちは、その場にへたへたとすわりこんでしまうし、家来はちりぢりににげ去ってしまった。

「その娘をもらったぞうっ。」

手をのばす鬼の前に立ちはだかったのは、法師一人。

「鬼め、待てっ。」

といっても、鬼には見えないそのすがた。

「なにをきょろきょろしておる。きさまの足もとを、よーく見ろ！

一寸法師が相手だ！」

「なんじゃ、これは、がっはっはっ。ちょろちょろうるさいやつじゃ。」

と、鬼は一寸法師をつまむと、口の中へぽんとほうりこんだ。

さ あ 、 た い へ ん 。

一寸法師は鬼にのみこまれてしまった。

「ほ、法師……！」

春姫さまと女たちはまっさお。

「さてと、うるさいやつもいなくなったし、いよいよただくか。」

そのときです。鬼がきゅうに腹をおさえてくるしみだした。

"A d-d-demon!" The supposedly brave and strong warriors ran for their lives at the sight of the huge red monster with horns, long claws, and sharp fangs.

"I'll take that juicy-looking girl right there," growled the demon, pointing at Haruhime.

"Oh no you won't, you ugly devil," said Issun Boshi, standing firm in front of the creature. But he was so small that the demon only looked around bewildered, wondering where the voice had come from.

"Down here, right in front of your big fat nose! It is I, the samurai Issun Boshi, who'll make you wish you'd never been born!"

"What's this?" grunted the demon. "Ah-ha-ha-ha! Pesky little insect!" The monster picked Hoshi up and tossed him into its foul-smelling mouth. Gulp!

"Hoshi-i-i!" cried Haruhime as her courageous bodyguard disappeared down the demon's throat.

"The little pest is gone, my sweet. Ha, ha! Now it's just you and me." No sooner had the demon said this than it doubled over, clutching its stomach and shrieking,

「あーっ、あっ、いたーい、うっ。
やめてくれーっ。」
　なんと、一寸法師は鬼の腹の中で、
針の刀をぬいて、めったやたらとつき
まくった。
「もう、らんぼうはしないかあ。」
「しなーい、ぜったいしないっ。」
「よーし、それなら舌をだせ。」
　鬼の舌の上を、一寸法師がでてきた。
「姫！　おけがはありませんか。。
「はいっ。」
　一寸法師は、大きな大きな鬼を見上げながらさけんだ。
「もう、二度とでてくるなよ。」
「はい、わかりました。えーん、えん。いたいよーっ、
いたいよーっ。」
　鬼は、なきなきにげていった。
　そのとき、春姫さまは、鬼のわすれ物に気がついた。
「まあ、打ち出のこづち。これはねがいごとをなんでも

かなえてくれる、ふ
しぎなこづちなので
す。法師はなにをの
ぞみますか。」
　「はい、わたしは、
りっぱなからだがほ
しいです。」

26

"Ow! Stop it! That hurts!"

Inside the monster's belly, Issun Boshi had drawn his needle-sword and was slashing and jabbing.

"Please stop! I'll be good, I promise!" screamed the demon.

"All right, then," came Hoshi's muffled voice. "Open your mouth and stick out your tongue."

The demon did as it was told, and out popped Issun Boshi, waving his needle. "Haruhime!" he called. "Are you all right?"

"Yes, Hoshi. Thanks to you."

Issun Boshi looked up at the enormous demon and shouted, "Don't you ever show your face around here again!"

"Yes, sir. Ow! Whatever you say. Wa-a-ah!" The demon fled in tears, holding its stomach.

When it had gone, Haruhime spotted something the monster had left behind. "It's a magic hammer!" she exclaimed. "This will grant any wish you make. Hoshi, my hero, what would you like?"

"I ... I'd like to be bigger...."

春姫さまはにっこりわらって、一寸法師の前にすわった。

「法師のからだよ、大きくなれ、大きくなれ、大きくなあれ！」

　なんとまあ、姫がこづちをふるたびに、法師のからだはだんだん大きくなり、みるみるうちにりっぱな若者のすがたにかわっていった。

　こうして、故郷をでてから幾年月。一寸法師はいまやりっぱな若者となり、鬼たいじのてがらをみとめられて、りっぱなおさむらいになった。

　そして、名まえを堀川の少将とかえて、春姫さまを妻にもらい、両親をよんで、いつまでもいつまでもしあわせに暮らしたということです。　　　　　（おわり）

Haruhime smiled and sat in front of him. Shaking the magic hammer, she chanted, "Grow tall, Issun Boshi. Six feet tall, Issun Boshi!" And with every shake of the hammer, Hoshi grew taller and taller. Finally, before the fair maiden stood a handsome, long-legged, broad-shouldered young man.

Thus it was that only a few short years after leaving his country home, Issun Boshi realized his dream. He became a renowned samurai, as famous in the capital for his fine looks and manly appearance as for his skill in conquering demons. He married the beautiful Haruhime, and Lord Sanjo gave them a splendid new estate of their own. Hoshi sent for his mother and father, who came to stay with him and his bride, and they all live happily ever after.

桃太郎

　むかしむかし、あるところに、おじいさんとおばあさんがおった。

　おじいさんは山へしば刈りに、おばあさんは川へせんたくにいった。

　おばあさんが、川でじゃぶじゃぶせんたくをしていると、川上から大きなももが、どんぶらこっこ、どんぶらこっこと流れてきたあ。

　おばあさんは、そのももをひろいあげると、だいじにかかえて家へ帰った。

　山から帰ったおじいさんも、びっくり。ももをなでなでしながらいうた。

「りっぱなももだのう。」

「いっちょ、切ってみっか。」

Momotaro, the Peach Boy

Once upon a time there was an old couple who lived in a village way out in the country. One day, while the old man was up in the mountains gathering firewood, the old woman went to the river to do her laundry. As she was scrubbing the clothes she noticed an enormous peach bobbing and rolling down the river. With some difficulty, she fished the giant peach out of the water, and that evening she carried it home with her.

When the old man came back and saw the peach, he was amazed at its size.

"What a find!" he exclaimed.

"Shall we cut it open?" suggested the old woman.

「おお、そうすべえ。」

と、二人の相談はまとまりまして、ももをまないたの上においた。

おばあさんが、ほうちょうをももにあてた、そのとき——、ももがごそごそ、ころんと、うごいたんじゃあ。

ももが、ももが生きている〜〜っ。とおもったら、ももがぱかんとまん中からわれて、中から男の子がとびだしたあ。

おじいさんもおばあさんも、びっくらこいた。もっとびっくらこいたのは、この男の子の元気のよさ。そして、その食いっぷり。

食うわ、食うわ。むしゃむしゃ、ぺろり。むしゃ、ぺろり。大きなおわんで、なんばいもめしのおかわりじゃあ。

おじいさんとおばあさんは、たいそうよろこび、桃太郎と名づけた。

桃太郎は、食えば食っただけ、みるみるうちに大きくそだっていった。おまけに、おとなもかなわないほどの力持ち。重いものでも、ひょい、ぽんと、かるがるともちあげる。こうして桃太郎は強い子にそだっていった。

ところが、ちょっとだけしんぱいなことがあったんじゃ。

"Why not?"

They placed the peach on the table and were just about to slice into it when … the peach started moving!

"It's alive!" the old woman screamed. The words were no sooner out of her mouth than the peach burst open and out popped a bouncing baby boy. The old man and woman were flabbergasted.

Once they'd recovered from their surprise (after all, it's not every day that a baby pops out of a peach), the old couple, who had no children of their own, were delighted. They decided to name the child Momotaro, since *momo* means "peach" and Taro is a good name for any red-blooded, healthy boy. And Momotaro certainly was healthy. My goodness, what an appetite he had! Chomp, chomp. Gulp. Smack! Chomp, gulp, burp! He gobbled down bowl after bowl of rice.

The more Momotaro ate, the bigger and stronger he got. By the time he was three or four years old, he had the strength of a full-grown man. There was only one problem: he refused to talk.

Even when the old woman tickled him and

「桃太郎やー、べろべろばあ〜〜。」
と、おばあさんがあやしても、桃太郎はだまったまんま。
おじいさんが、にっこりわらいかけてもしらん顔。
「やれやれ、こまったもんじゃわい。」
「ほんになあ……。」
　いつまでたっても、ちーっとも話をしない桃太郎に、
おじいさんもおばあさんも、どうしたもんかと気にかけ
ておった。
「この子、どうして口きかんのじゃ。」
と、二人が顔を見あわせたときじゃ。
「やるぞ〜〜っ。」
　た、太郎がとつぜん大声をだしたあ。
　口をきいたあ！
「じいちゃん、ばあちゃん、おら、鬼たいじにいくう。」
　おじいさんとおばあさんは、ただおどろいて、ぽけー
っとしておった。
「したくしてけれえー。」
　桃太郎の大きな声に、おばあさんははっとしていうた。
「鬼たいじなんて、そんなおそろしいことを……。」
　そのころ、村にはしばしばおそろしい鬼があらわれて、
ものとり、人さらい
と、ありとあらゆる
らんぼうをはたらい
て、村人たちをくる
しめておった。

said, "Momotaro, my little peach! Goochie-Goochie-goo!" the boy wouldn't make a sound. When the old man tried to play pat-a-cake, Momotaro would just yawn and look away.

As the years went by, the old man and woman began to worry. "Why doesn't he ever say anything? What are we going to do?"

Then one day ...

"Well, I'm off!" said Momotaro. He had actually spoken at last! The old couple were too surprised to reply. "Grandma, Grandpa," the boy went on in a loud, confident voice, "I'm going to go and conquer the demons."

The old woman gasped. "But, Taro ... Why would you want to do such a dangerous thing?"

Ferocious demons, you see, had been raiding the village almost every night. They stole things and kidnapped people and knocked down houses, and the villagers were terrified of them. When Momotaro heard about this, it made him so angry that he decided to do something about it: he would go to Demon's Island, where the monsters lived, and teach them a lesson.

　力の強い桃太郎は、これを知って、もうがまんができ
なかったのじゃあ。

　おじいさんとおばあさんは、かわいい桃太郎のために
きびだんごやはれ着をそろえてやったと。

　とうとう、出発の日がやってきた。

　桃太郎は、おじいさんのつくったはれ着をきて、おば
あさんのつくったきびだんごのつつみをこしにつけた。

　悲しみにしずむおじいさんとおばあさんをのこして、
桃太郎はいさんで家をでていった。

「たっしゃでなあ……。」

「ぶじに帰ってきてくれやあ……。」

　見送るおじいさんとおばあさんは、とうとうなきだし
てしもうたと。

　さて、桃太郎はというと、なげき悲しむおじいさんと
おばあさんの気持ちも知らず、鬼が島めざして一直線。

　とちゅう、いぬが一ぴきやってきた。

「桃太郎さん、桃太郎さん、こしにつけたきびだんご、
一つください。くれたら家来になるよ。」

"Well?" said Momotaro. "Aren't you going to help me get ready?"

There was nothing the old man and woman could say or do to make Momotaro change his mind. So the old man made him a suit of colorful clothes, and the old woman baked some dumpling for the journey. Then, with tears in their eyes, they bid farewell to their brave little boy.

"Be careful, Taro …"

Perhaps Momotaro was too young to understand what made the old man and woman so sad. Smiling and waving, he marched straight off toward Demon's Island with the bag of dumplings hanging from his belt.

On the way he met a dog.

"Momotaro, Momotaro, please give me one of your dumplings. If you do, I'll go with you and help you fight the demons," barked the dog. So

いぬはきびだんごをもらって、家来になった。

しばらくすると、さるがでてきて、きびだんごをもらって家来になった。

つづいてきじもでてきた。これまたきびだんごをもらって家来になった。

いぬ、さる、きじをおともにつれて、ゆくはわれらが桃太郎。

花もあらしもふみこえて、心にきめた鬼たいじ。鬼が島めざしてまっしぐら。おそれを知らぬ桃太郎。

一度ちかった大きいゆめは、なにがなんでもやらねばならぬ。それが男の生きる道。

桃太郎の一行は、こうして、野をこえ山をこえ、海べについた。

船にのりこんだ桃太郎たち、力をあわせてこぎすすむ。

えんやあ、とっと。

えんやあ、とっと。

広い海原、ひろがる世界。でっかいゆめのせ、えんやあ、とっと。

こうして、何日か、海をこぎすすんでいった。

Momotaro gave him a dumpling and set off again with the dog close behind him.

Before they had gone far they met a monkey and a pheasant. And for the price of one dumpling each, these two also agreed to accompany Momotaro. So off they all went, in single file, calling out to the people they met, "Stand back, stand back! It's Momotaro, the strongest boy in the land. Make way, make way! It's Momotaro, the Peach Boy, and his fearless band!"

Into the wilderness and through raging storms, across the plains and over the mountains marched Momotaro with his faithful companions. Nothing could stop him because, you see, a man must have a dream. And Momotaro would never give up until he'd made his dream come true.

After a long journey they arrived at the sea. They piled in a boat and began to row south to Demon's Island. Heave, ho! Heave, ho! Across the wide blue sea they rowed. Heave, ho! Heave, ho! They pulled on their oars day after day till at last they caught sight of their

　とうとうついた、鬼が島。海の中からつきでている岩山の島、それがめざす鬼が島だ。

　きじが偵察飛行にとびたった。

「鬼どもに見つかるなよ。」

　船はそうっと島に近づき、いよいよ桃太郎たちも島に上陸だ!

　そこへきじがもどってきた。

「なに?　鬼どもは酒盛りのさいちゅうだと。ようし、いまだあ。」

と、鬼が門へむかっていく。ところが、門はしっかりしまっていて、びくともしない。

「ここは、まかしといて。わけないさ。」

　さるが、ぴょんと門をとびこえて、裏からかぎをはずす。

　桃太郎は、鬼が門をぎい～～っとあけた。鬼たちは酒盛りのまっさいちゅう。とつぜんあら

destination—a jagged mountain jutting out of the sea. Demon's Island.

Momotaro sent the pheasant ahead to spy on the demons. "Make sure they don't see you!" he warned the bird. He guided the boat quietly up to the rock-strewn beach and stepped ashore with the dog and the monkey. Soon the pheasant returned and told Momotaro what he'd seen.

"What's that? The demons are having a party? Now's our chance, then!" Momotaro led the way to Demon's Gate. But the huge door was closed and would not budge.

"Leave it to me," said the monkey. He scrambled up over the gate and unlatched it from the other side.

Creak! The Peach Boy flung open the gate. Inside, the demons were busy eating and drinking and making merry. Their mouths fell open when

われた桃太郎たちに鬼たちはぽかーんとしておった。

「われこそは、日本一の桃太郎！　鬼どもをせいばつにきた！」

あっけにとられた鬼たちの頭の上を、いぬがわんわん、さるがきゃっきゃっ、きじがけんけんと、かみついたり、ひっかいたり、つついたり。

つづいて、怪力桃太郎がぽかりぽかり。その強いこと、強いこと。

いやはや、鬼たちのあわてたのなんの。上を下への大さわぎ。そこへ、いかりくるった鬼の親分があらわれた。

「うーん、こしゃくな、こぞう。おれさまがあいてだあ。」

桃太郎めがけて、太い鉄棒をびゅーんとふりまわす。

がき〜〜ん！

なんと、桃太郎の頭にぶつかった鉄棒が、ぽきっとおれてしもうた。これには鬼の親分もまいった。

Momotaro and his animal friends appeared before them.

"Who are you?" said one of the devils.

"I'm the one and only Momotaro, the strongest boy in the land. *En garde*, you dirty demons!"

Arf, arf! Screech, screech! Cackle, cackle! The dog, the monkey, and the pheasant bit, scratched, and poked at the demons as Momotaro came out slugging. *Biff! Bam! Pow!*

The demons were frantic. They dashed about bumping into each other until their leader pushed through the crowd to challenge Momotaro. He was very angry, and he was waving a big iron club. "You cheeky little runt," he growled. "I'll teach you not to fool with the King of Demons!"

Clang! The demon's deadly weapon came crashing down on the Peach Boy's head. But the club broke right in two and Momotaro wasn't hurt at all. The demon king couldn't believe his eyes. He was standing there staring at his broken club when Momotaro charged.

そのとたん、鉄棒をもおるかたい頭で、親分の頭にごち～んと、頭つきーぱつ!

勝負あった!

鬼の親分、目をまわしてばったり。

「どうだ、もうわるさしねえか。」

「もう、わるいことはいたしません。おゆるしください。」

こうして、鬼からとりもどした宝物を船につんで、帰ることになった。

「お送りします。」

と、鬼は、「ふう～～っ。」とふいて船をうごかしてくれた。

桃太郎は、おじいさんとおばあさんのところへ、ぶじ帰っていった。

桃太郎にとって、なによりうれしかったのは、でっかい鬼たいじのゆめを、やりとげたことだったそうな。 　　　　　　　　(おわり)

Thud! The Peach Boy butted the demon between the horns with his harder-than-steel head.

It was all over. The King of Demons sat in the dirt with his eyes rolling and his tongue hanging out.

"Well? Are you going to quit your evil ways?" demanded Momotaro.

"Yes, yes, we'll be good from now on, I promise. So please don't hit me again!"

The frightened demons loaded Momotaro's boat with treasure. Then they all lined up by the shore, bowing, as the boy, the dog, the monkey, and the pheasant climbed on board.

"Allow me to help you, Master," said the demon king. He took a deep breath and blew with all his might, sending the boat zipping toward the mainland.

Momotaro returned home triumphant. The old couple and all the villagers rejoiced when they heard the wonderful story of how the Peach Boy had conquered the demons. But happiest of all was Momotaro. He had, after all, made his dream come true.

花咲か爺さん

　むかしむかし、ある山里に、やさしいおじいさん
とおばあさんがおりました。

　ある日、おじいさんが家の前で小さな畑をたがやして
いますと、となりのらんぼうなよくばりじいさんのどな
る声がしました。

「こら、人の畑へ入りよって！」

　きゃんきゃん、きゃん。

　走ってきた小犬をおじいさんがだきあげると、となり
のじいさんが追いかけてきていいました。

「その小犬は、おらの畑をあら
しよったんじゃ。こっちへよこ
せ！」

　小犬はおじいさんのうでの中
でぶるぶるふるえています。

「わしにめんじてゆるしてやっ
てけれ。」

Grandfather Cherry Blossom

Once upon a time a kind old man lived with his gentle wife in a village at the foot of a mountain. The old man was plowing his field one day when he heard someone shouting. It was the greedy old grouch who lived next door.

"Bah! Get out of my garden!"

Yip! Yip! Yip! A little white puppy came running toward the old man and jumped into his arms just as the grouchy neighbor appeared.

"That mutt was tearing up my garden. Hand him over!" demanded the neighbor.

The frightened puppy was shaking and whimpering. "I'm sure he didn't mean any harm. Won't you overlook it just this once?"

　おじいさんは、となりのじいさんに頭を下げてたのみ
ました。

「こんど入ったら、かならずぶったたいてやるからな。」

　となりのじいさんは、おこっていってしまいました。

　こうして、やさしいおじいさんとおばあさんは、この
小犬をだいじに飼ってやることにしました。

　小犬はしろと名づけられ、朝から晩まで、よく働きま
した。

　やがてしろは、飯を
食べてどんどん大きく
なっていきました。

　小皿一ぱい食べれば
一ぱいぶん、おわんで
食べればおわんぶんだ
け、おひつで食べれば
おひつぶん、大きくなりました。

　ある日のこと、しろがおじいさんのところへきて、き
ものをくわえてひっぱります。どこへやら、おじいさん
をつれていこうとしているようです。

The kind old man smiled and bowed. "I'll make sure he doesn't bother you anymore."

"Suit yourself," grumbled the grouch, walking away angrily. "But if I ever see that stupid dog in my garden again, I'll kill him."

The kind old man and his wife decided to keep the stray puppy. They named him Shiro, which means "white," because his fur was the color of fresh-fallen snow.

Now Shiro had a very big appetite, and the kind old couple always gave him as much food as he could eat. The more he ate the larger he grew, and soon he was so big he could carry the old man on his back.

One morning, as the old man was hoeing his field, Shiro came and tugged at his sleeve, as if he wanted to show him something.

"What is it, Shiro? I'm kind of busy, boy."

But Shiro wouldn't leave him alone. Finally

　　　しろは、おじいさん
を背中にのせて、裏山
に登っていきました。
　　　山のてっぺんまでく
ると、しろはおじいさんを背中からおろし、
「ここほれ、わんわん。
　　ここわれ、わんわん。」
と、ほえるのでした。
　　おじいさんは、ふしぎに思いましたが、いわれたとお
りほってみました。
　　土をほると、なにやらくわにぶつかるものがありまし
た。
「うん？　なんじゃあ……、こ、これ
は。こ、こ、小判じゃあ。」
　　その夜、おじいさんとおばあ
さんは、生まれてはじめて、小
判を持った幸せをかみしめまし
た。
　　ところが……。
　　そこへ、となりのよくばりじいさんとばあさんがやっ
てきました。二人は、しょうじの穴からのぞいて、小判
の山を見てしまったのです。
　　おじいさんに、裏山で小判をほった話を聞くと、いや
がるしろを、むりやり引っぱっていってしまいました。
　　あくる日、あんなにいじめたしろの背にまたがって、

the old man climbed on the huge dog's back and
off they went, up the mountain behind the house.
When they neared the top, Shiro stopped next to
a tree and began barking.

"Arf, arf! Dig here! Arf, arf!"

The old man scratched his head, shrugged,
and started to dig with
his hoe. Before long he
struck something hard.

"Hm? What's this?"
He kneeled down and
reached into the hole.
"Why, it's … it's gold!
Gold coins, and lots of them!"

That night the old man and his wife were sitting at home talking excitedly about how Shiro
had found the treasure, when the greedy old
grouch happened by with his even greedier old
wife. They peeked through a hole in the door and
spotted the pile of gold. When the grouch over-
heard the story, he was green with envy. He found
Shiro, threw a rope around his neck, and dragged
the dog home with him.

The next day, the old grouch and his wife
jumped on Shiro's back and drove him up the

よくばりじいさんは裏山へ登っていきました。

そして、しろが力つきてたおれたその場所を、ここだとばかりほりはじめました。

がちっと、くわにかたいものがぶつかりました。

「出た、出たぞ！　うはっはっはは。」

小判だと思って、よろこんで手にしたとたん、よくばりじいさんはこしをぬかしました。

出てくるわ、出てくるわ。へびや化けものが、ぞろぞろ、ぞろぞろ。

「よくも、ひどいめにあわせたなっ。」

おこったとなりの

じいさんは、とうとう、しろを殺してしまいました。

やさしいおじいさんとおばあさんは心から悲しんで、

mountain, kicking and whipping him mercilessly. They had almost neared the peak when Shiro's strength gave out and he fell over, panting.

"This must be the spot!" cried the greedy old man. He started digging, and before very long— *clank!*— his hoe struck something hard. "Hooray! We did it! We're rich!"

Convinced that he had found gold, the old grouch reached into the hole. What came out, however, weren't gold bars at all but slimy snakes—*Hisssss, hisssss*—and weird, smelly goblins—*Wooooo!*

The old grouch and his wife screamed and fell back, covering their eyes. When they finally opened them, the snakes and goblins were gone and their fear gave way to rage.

"Look what you've done, you stupid dog!" yelled the grouch. "I'll teach you not to make a fool of me again!" He picked up his hoe and gave Shiro such a blow over the head that it killed the poor dog instantly.

The kind old man and woman, of course, were heartbroken when they learned what had happened. They carried Shiro down from the mountain and buried him near their home. Next to the

しろの墓を立てて、そのそばに小さな木をうえました。

　するとふしぎ。その木はずんずん大きくなって、ひとかかえもする大きな木になりました。

　ある日、二人がお花をそなえようと、墓までやってきて、その大木を見上げておりました。すると、その木が、なにかいっているようでした。

「うすにしてくれえ、うすにしてくれえ……。」

　二人はしろの木のいうとおり、その木でうすを作ることにしました。

「うん、そうじゃ。しろはもちが好きじゃった。もちをついてそなえてやろうかい、のう。」

　おじいさんとおばあさんは、できあがったばかりのうすで、もちをつきはじめました。

grave they planted a little tree, and after saying a prayer for the dog they had loved so much, they went home with tears in their eyes.

That might have been the end of the story. But soon a wondrous thing began to happen. The tree the old couple had planted started to grow at an unbelievable speed. In no time at all it was so large you couldn't reach around it.

One morning the old man and his wife were putting fresh flowers on Shiro's grave when they looked up at the great tree and marveled at how it had grown. And at that moment something even more wondrous happened. They heard a voice coming from inside the trunk. "Make me into a mortar," it seemed to be saying. "Make me into a mortar...."

The old man scratched his head, shrugged, and went to the house to get his axe. He cut down the tree and shaped part of the trunk into a large mortar for pounding mochi—soft rice cakes.

"Come to think of it, Shiro always loved mochi, didn't he?" said the gentle old woman when they got the mortar home. "Let's make some to put on his grave."

"That's a good idea."

「ほいしょ。」「あいよ。」

　ぺったん、ぺったん。おじいさんとおばあさんは、仲よくもちをつきます。

　そのうちに、うすの中のもちが光りだしました。

「あら、おじいさん。なんでしょう。」

「はやー、ふしぎなもちじゃ。」

　おじいさんとおばあさんは、光るもちを取り出して、ちぎって小さく丸めます。すると、もちがぴかぴか光りだしたではありませんか。

「こ、小判じゃあ！」

　そこへまた、となりのよくばりじいさんが顔を出していいました。

「どうじゃ、わしにうすを貸さんか。」

「これは、しろの形見じゃから。」

と、おじいさんがいうのもおかまいなしに、となりのじ

Oomph! Ah! Oomph! Ah! The old man pounded the rice in the mortar with a heavy wooden mallet, and after each swing his wife kneaded the gradually thickening dough. It was getting smooth and sticky when suddenly the old woman stopped and pointed inside the mortar. Something was glittering in there.

"Look, dear," she said. "What's that?"

"I don't know. I've never seen mochi like this."

They took the dough out of the mortar and rolled it into little round cakes. And as they watched, the mochi hardened and began to shine even more brightly.

"Why, this isn't mochi," the old man cried. "It's gold!"

So it was. And who should show his face again just at the moment but the greedy old grouch from next door. He and his wife had been peeping in the whole time. "Say," he said, "how about lending me that mortar?"

"But … but this is all that's left of dear old Shiro.…"

"You'll get it back. Don't be so stingy." The grouch and his wife walked right in and carried

いさんとばあさんは、うすを持っていってしまいました。

さっそくもちをつきはじめた二人は、もちがつきあがるのも待ちきれずに、うすの中をのぞいてばかり——。

「じいさん、いっこうにもちの色が変わらんなあ。そうじゃ、丸めればいいんじゃろう。」

二人は、もちを小さくちぎり、丸めてならべました。

すると、白いもちは黒いすみになって、ばちんばちんとはねて、二人の顔をまっ黒にしてしまいました。

となりのじいさんとばあさんは、おこって、うすを小さく割って、かまどでもやしてしまったのです。

やさしいおじいさんは、そのことを知ると、それはそれはがっかりしてしまいました。

そこで、となりの家のかまどの前へきて、灰を手ですくいあげました。

「しろ……。」

せめて、この灰をしろの形見に、そう考えたおじいさんは、灰をかごに入れて、だいじに家にもって帰りました。

the mortar away. And as soon as they got home, they started to pound their own mochi.

The greedy old woman kept peering inside the mortar. "It hasn't changed color at all," she said. "I know—we've got to shape it into little cakes."

So that's just what they did, placing the small round pieces in a row on the table. And sure enough, right before their eyes, the mochi began to change—but not into gold. It became a mass of gooey black charcoal. The old grouch and his wife started at the mess in disgust and were just about to begin yelling at each other when—*poof!*—the charcoal exploded, filling the kitchen with flames and black soot. Sputtering and shouting, the grouch grabbed his axe, chopped the mortar into tiny bits, and threw the pieces into the fire.

The kindhearted old man broke down and cried when he heard what had happened. He went to the grouch's house, gathered up the ashes of the mortar, and placed them in a basket. "Shiro ...," he sobbed as he carried the basket home.

「この灰を畑にまいて、しろの好きだった大根を育てて
やりましょう。」

　おばあさんがそういうので、おじいさんは灰を畑にま
きました。

　灰は風にふかれてちっていきます。すると、かれた木
が光りだし、さくらの
花がさいたではありま
せんか。

「ばあさんや、みろ、
さくらじゃ！」

　よろこんだおじいさ
ん、ぱーっと、はでに
灰をまきました。

　ふしぎやふしぎ、灰がかかると、かれ木に花がさきま
した。

　こうして、たちまちのうちにあたり一面はさくらの海
となりました。

His gentle wife tried to comfort him. "Let's scatter these ashes on the field," she said, "and grow some of those giant radishes that Shiro used to love so much." The old man agreed and they walked slowly out to the field with the basket.

Now it was a very windy day, and as the old man was scattering the ashes, some of them blew onto a withered old cherry tree. And that's when the most wondrous thing of all happened.

No sooner had the ashes fallen on the tree than the dry branches sprang back to life and became covered with beautiful blossoms.

"Goodness gracious! Come quick, dear. Watch this!"

As his wife looked on, the old man ran about sprinkling ashes on cherry trees. And every tree touched by the ashes began to bloom. Soon the little field was alive with colorful flowers.

「はあ、春でもないのに花がさいた。」

　村の人たちがおどろいて集まってきました。

　村から山へ、村から村へ、村から町へ、そしてお城へ——。この話は伝わっていきました。

　話を聞いたお城のお殿さまが、家来をつれておじいさんのところへやってきました。

「くるしゅうない。はでにやってくれ。」

　おじいさんは、かれ木の上で灰をまきました。

「かれ木に花をさかせるぞー。」

　まいちった灰は、いつのまにか、さくらの花びらに変わっていました。

In the days that followed, all the people in the village came to marvel at this wonderful sight. "Such lovely cherry blossoms," they would say. "And it's not even spring!"

The word spread like wildfire from village to village, until it reached the ears of a great daimyo. Once he'd heard of this miracle, the daimyo decided he must see it with his own eyes. Taking ten or twelve of his best soldiers, he made the long journey over the mountains to the little village where the old man lived. When he got to the house, the old man came out, bowing to greet him.

"I've heard a lot about you, old man," said the daimyo. "Let me see what you can do."

The old man climbed up a withered cherry tree. "If it please your lordship," he announced, "I'll make this dead cherry tree come back to life and bloom."

And that's exactly what he did, much to the daimyo's amazement. The ashes he sprinkled on the branches turned, in the twinkling of an eye, into lovely pink and white flowers.

"Extraordinary! I've never seen anything like it!" the daimyo exclaimed. "Old man, you're the

「日本一の花さかじいよ。
ほうびをとらせるぞ！」

　お殿さまは大よろこび。

「そのほうび、ちょっと待
った。」

　そこへかけつけたのは、
となりのよくばりじいさ
ん。

「わたくしめこそ、日本一の花さかじい。この灰で、
一度にどっとさかせましょうぞ。」

　よくばりじいさんは、木にとびのって灰をどっとまき
ました。

「じじのさかせるじじの花あ──。」

　ところが、灰はそのままお殿さまの上へ──。

「はー、はっくしょん、はっくしょん。」

　人のまねばかりしていた、よくばりじいさんは、とう
とうろうやに入れられてしまいましたとさ。　　（おわり）

best blossom-maker in the land. Henceforth, sir, you shall be known as Grandfather Cherry Blossom. Allow me to reward you with this." The daimyo held out a sack full of silver and gold.

"Just a moment, your lordship!" came a familiar voice. The greedy old grouch from next door ran up to the daimyo and bowed. "I'm the real Grandfather Cherry Blossom. Watch this …" He snatched the basket from the kindhearted old man, climbed a tree, and threw the ashes into the air.

But instead of turning into blossoms, the ashes merely fell toward the ground, and a gust of wind blew them right into the daimyo's face. The daimyo sneezed and coughed, rubbed his eyes, and brushed the ashes off his clothes. He was enraged. "Arrest that old impostor!" he shouted to his soldiers.

So the grouch was tied up and carted off to jail. And it served him right, don't you think?

七夕さま

美しい夏の夜空。星くずがいっぱいにちらばり、まるで空を流れる川のように見える天の川——。その川をはさんでひときわかがやく二つの星があります。牽牛と織女。一年に一度、七月七日だけにあうという、この二つの星には、こんな話が語り伝えられているのです。

☆　☆　☆

むかし、ある村に、みけらんという名まえの若者が住んでおりました。
ある日、みけらんは畑仕事の帰り道で、ふしぎなものを見つけました。

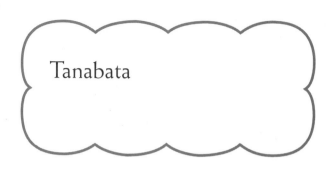

Tanabata

Across the sky of a clear summer night, the Milky Way flows like a mighty river. On either side of its vast, raging current are the bright stars Altair and Vega. According to an old legend, these two heavenly bodies were once an earthly man and his wife. Now, it is said, they are allowed to meet only once a year—on the seventh day of the seventh month. This is the story of those star-crossed lovers.

Once upon a time a young man named Mikeran was walking home after working in the fields. As he passed by the shore of a lake, he spotted something hanging from a tree.

「なんだ、これは？　おー、衣じゃ。なんという美しい衣じゃろう。」

　それは、いままで見たこともないような美しい衣でした。みけらんは、その衣が、どうしてもほしくなってし

まいました。衣をかごの中に入れ、帰ろうとしたときです。

「あの、もし……。」

「はーて、だれかおれをよんだかの？」

　池のそばの草むらから、美しい女があらわれました。

「はい、わたしがあなたさまをおよびしたのです。どうか、わたしの羽衣を返してください。」

「は、は、はごろも？」

「はい、その羽衣がないと、わたしは天へ帰れないのです。」

　女の人はいまにもなきだしそうな顔で、こんなことをいったのです。

「わたしは天に住む女です。下界の女ではありません。この池に降りて水浴びをしていたのですが、ついつい、ときのたつのをわすれてしまいました。

　どうかおねがいです。わたしの羽衣を返してください。」

「は、羽衣じゃと？　そ、そんなものわしは知らんぞ。」

"What's that?" he wondered. "It looks like a robe...."

But it was not like any robe he had seen before. It shone like a star in the evening light. Mikeran was delighted with his find. "It must be worth a fortune," he thought. He took the robe down, folded it up, and placed it in his basket. He was about to walk away when someone called out to him.

"Excuse me, sir."

"What? Who said that?"

"I did." Out of the tall grass by the lake stepped the most beautiful young woman Mikeran had ever seen. "Please," she said. "Please give me back my celestial robe."

"C—celestial robe?"

"Yes. Oh, please, sir. Without it I can't return to my home in heaven. You see," she went on, her eyes brimming with tears, "I don't belong on earth. I only came here to bathe awhile in this lovely lake. Please, I beg you, give me back my robe!"

Mikeran's heart was beating wildly. "I—I don't know what you're talking about," he lied. "I haven't seen any robe."

　みけらんは、いまさら自分が羽衣をかくしたともいえ
ず、とうとう知らぬ存ぜぬで押しとおしてしまいました。

　そして、天へ帰れなくなった天女は、なくなく下界に
のこり、みけらんの家へ行って、いっしょにくらすよう
になりました。

　天女は「たなばた」という名でした。

　みけらんとたなばたは、とても仲のよい夫婦になって、
何年かが過ぎました。

　ある日のこと、みけらんが畑仕事へ出かけた後のこと

The truth is that Mikeran had fallen in love the moment he'd laid eyes on the maiden. He feared that if he gave her the robe, she'd fly off into the sky and disappear forever.

"Shall I help you look for it?" he said.

"Oh, would you, sir?"

Mikeran pretended to search for the robe, but, of course, it was in his basket all the time. "It's no use," he said at last. "Someone must have stolen it."

Tanabata—for that was the maiden's name—sat on the ground and began to sob.

"Don't cry," said Mikeran, taking her hand. "If you've nowhere to go, you can come stay with me."

So from that day on, Tanabata lived in Mikeran's house. And as time went by she came to love the gentle, handsome youth as much as he loved her. They were married and spent many wonderful years together. Happy as she was with her earthly life, however, Tanabata could never forget her home in heaven. Often at night when Mikeran was asleep she would open the window and gaze up, sighing, at the starry sky.

Then, one day when Mikeran was out working

でした。たなばたは、天じょうのはりのすきまを、はとがつついているのを見つけました。

はとがひっぱり出したのは、なんとあの羽衣でした。

「あ、あれは……。やっぱりあの人がかくしてたのだわ。」

羽衣をまとえば、はや天女。たなばたの心は、もはや天上人となっておりました。

夕方になって、畑から帰ってきたみけらんは、家の前に立っているたなばたを見つけてびっくり。

「あ、たなばた！ ああっ、羽衣！」

みけらんは羽衣を見て、もう、どういうことかわかりました。

たなばたは、天にのぼりながら、こういいました。

「あなた……、もしもわたしのことを恋しいと思うなら、わらじを千足編んで、竹の下にうめてくださいな。そうすれば、きっとまた会うことができます。……きっと……、そうしてくださいね……。まってますよ〜〜うっ。」

たなばたは、高く高くのぼって、天に帰ってしまいました。

in the fields, Tanabata noticed her pet dove pecking at something between the roofbeams. As she watched, the dove thrust its beak into a crack in the ceiling and pulled out a piece of beautiful, glittering cloth.

"My robe!" Tanabata cried. "So Mikeran knew where it was all along. He was hiding it from me!"

That evening Mikeran returned from the fields to find his wife waiting outside in her celestial garment.

"Tanabata! You—you found the robe!"

Tanabata nodded sadly, lifted her hands toward heaven, and began to rise in the air. As she rose, she looked down at her husband and said, "Mikeran ... if you really love me, weave a thousand pairs of straw sandals and bury them beneath a bamboo shoot. If you do that, we'll be able to meet again. I'll be waiting for you, my love...."

Mikeran watched helplessly as Tanabata ascended higher and higher. At last all he could see was her robe shining like a star in the evening sky.

　みけらんは、とても悲しみました。そして、つぎの日からさっそくわらじを作りはじめました。昼も夜も、みけらんはわらじを編みつづけました。

　編んだわらじを数えては、まだたらんと編みつづけ、また数えるのです。

　ある日のこと、とうとう千足のわらじを、たけのこのまわりにうめることができました。

「ふーっ、これでいいんじゃろうか。」

　わらじをうめたとたん、竹はどんどんと大きくなり、ぐんぐん、ぐんぐん空高くのびていきました。

「そうか、これを登っていけば、たなばたに会えるのか……。」

　みけらんは、大きくなった竹を登りはじめました。そして、もうすこしで天にとどくというところで、どうしても天まで手がとど
きません。

　みけらんは、たなばたに早くあいたい一心で、千足うめたつもりのわらじが、

Mikeran knew he would never be happy until he was reunited with his beautiful wife. So that very night he gathered all the straw he could find and began to weave the sandals. Night and day, day and night, he weaved and counted, counted and weaved.

At last he counted a thousand pairs. He hurried outside, found a bamboo shoot, and dug a large hole for the sandals beneath it. No sooner had he covered the sandals with earth than the bamboo began to grow at an incredible speed. In a matter of seconds, the tip had disappeared into the clouds.

"Now all I have to do is climb to the top!" thought Mikeran. From one branch to the next he climbed and climbed and climbed. And when finally he got to the top, he could see heaven's floor just above him. But he couldn't quite reach it. It seems that in his haste to meet Tanabata, he had made a mistake when he counted the san-

じつは九百九十九足しかなかったのです。

「おーい、たなばた！ たなばたあ。」

天の上で機を織っていた、たなばたの耳に、その声が聞こえてきました。

「はっ、もしやあの人では……。」

雲の上からのぞいてみると、それは恋しい夫のみけらんだったのです。

「あなたーっ、あなたーっ。」

「たなばたーっ、たなばたーっ。」

たなばたは手をのばし、みけらんを雲の上へと引き上げました。

「たなばた、あいたかったよう。」

二人は手をにぎりあってよろこびあいました。

そのとき、雲の間から顔を出した男がいます。たなばたの親父さまです。

「だれじゃな、その男は？」

「はい、わたしの夫、みけらんです。」

dals. He'd actually only woven nine hundred and ninety-nine pairs.

"Tanabata!" he shouted. "Tanabata, are you there?"

Tanabata was working her loom when she heard someone calling her name. "Oh!" she gasped. "Can it be?" She peered over the edge of her cloud and there, sure enough, was her husband, waving to her from the top of the great bamboo.

"Mikeran! Hold on!" Tanabata took the long piece of cloth from her loom and lowered it to Mikeran. He grabbed hold of it, pulled himself up to her cloud, and ran to her.

"Tanabata! I missed you so much!"

"Oh, Mikeran!"

They were holding each other tenderly when a bearded and fearful-looking old man appeared. It was Tanabata's father.

"What is the meaning of this?" he roared.

"This is my husband, Father," said Tanabata meekly. "His name is Mikeran."

「みけらんと申します。はじめてお目にかかります。」

　たなばたの親父さまは、自分の娘が下界の男とけっこんしたのが、なんともおもしろくありませんでした。それで、いろいろとむずかしい仕事をいいつけて、困らせてやろうと考えました。

「ふん、で、おぬしは下界ではなにをしておられた？」

「はい、畑仕事や山仕事でございます。」

「それならちょうどよい。ちょっくらこれをやってもらおう。」

　親父さまは、三日のうちに畑にたねをまくように、みけらんにいいつけました。みけらんは、がんばって、三日間で畑にたねをまき終わったのですが、

「わしは、向こうのたんぼにまけというたんじゃよ。」

と、親父さまがいうので、みけらんは、もうがっかりです。

"I'm honored to meet you, sir," said Mikeran, bowing.

But Tanabata's father was not at all happy to learn that his daughter had married a lowly earthling. "Tell me, young man," he said with a scowl, "how did you make your living on earth?"

"I worked in the fields, sir."

"Good. I've got just the job for you, then. Take all the seeds in those baskets and plant them in the star-field. You have three days to finish."

"Y—yes, sir," gulped Mikeran.

There must have been a million seeds in the huge basket. Mikeran set to work immediately, and for three days he never even stopped to rest. Finally, late on the third day, he planted the last seed and lay down exhausted. But no sooner had he done so than Tanabata's father appeared again.

"Not *this* star-field, you fool!" he shouted. "I meant the star-field over *there*. Now pick up all those seeds and replant them!"

Poor Mikeran. It would take years to find all

このようすを見ていたたなばたは、なんとか夫を助けようと、はとにたのみました。

「おまえの仲間をよんで、畑のたねをたんぼへまきなおしておくれ。」

はとが、たなばたのいうとおりにしましたので、たねのまきかえは、あっというまに終わりました。

くやしがった親父さまは、こんどは、もっとむずかしい仕事をいいつけました。

それは、三日三晩、うり畑の番をせよ、というのでした。

うり畑の番をしていると、ものすごくのどがかわくのです。でも、うりを食べるとたいへんなことがおこります。

「けっして、うりを食べてはいけませんよ。」

the seeds. Luckily, however, Tanabata had an idea. She called for her pet dove. "I want you to bring all your friends," she told the bird. "Ask them to dig out those seeds and replant them."

Before long the skies were filled with thousands of doves diving and swooping and soaring from one star-field to the other. And the job was finished in no time at all.

Tanabata's father was not amused, however. He spent the night thinking up another difficult task for Mikeran, and in the morning he called the earthling before him. "I need you to stand guard over the melon patch in the Valley of Heaven," he said. "You must 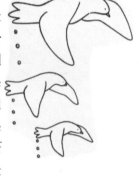 remain there for three days and three nights. And you're not to eat or drink anything while you're there."

When Tanabata heard of this new command, she was very worried. "Do be careful, Mikeran," she said. "And whatever you do, don't eat any of the sacred melons. If you do, something terrible will happen. Please promise me you won't."

たなばたにこういわれたのですが、みけらんは、のどがかわいてしかたありません。とうとうがまんしきれなくなって、うりに手を出してしまいました。すると、あっというまにうりの中から水があふれ出て、ごうごうと流れはじめました。

「みけらーん！」

「たなばたーっ！」

二人の間は、みるみるひきはなされてしまいました。

こうして、川をはさんで向かいあう二人のすがたが、牽牛星と織女星となったのです。

二人は、一年に一度、親父さまのゆるしをえて、七夕の日にだけあうことができるのだそうです。

いまでも二つの星は、天の川をはさんで、美しくかがやいています。　　　　　　　　　　　　　　　（おわり）

Mikeran swore he wouldn't touch the sacred fruit. But after two days of guarding the patch in the scorching sun, his throat was so parched he thought he would die of thirst. At last he couldn't stand it any longer. He cut open one of the ripe, juicy melons.

Ssshhhwwwwwooooossshhh!

A great torrent of water came gushing out of the melon. And in the twinkling of an eye the torrent became a raging river. Mikeran was swept off his feet, and the powerful current carried him to the far side of the Valley of Heaven.

"Mikera–a–an!"

"Tanabata–a–a!"

To this day, Tanabata and Mikeran sit on opposite banks of the river we call the Milky Way. You can see them each night gazing help-lessly across at each other, waiting for the one day in the year her father allows them to meet.

金太郎

む かしむかし、足柄山の山おくに、とっても元気のよい男の子がおりました。

男の子の名まえは金太郎、生まれたときからの力持ちで、はいはいしながら、うすにむすんだひもを引っぱって、うすを動かしたというほどです。

金太郎が、よちよち歩きをはじめたころ、お母さんは、金太郎に赤い腹がけをぬってあげました。

「さあ、腹がけができましたよ。さあ着てごらんよ。」

腹がけは、まだ金太郎にはぶかぶかでしたが、それは、早くこの腹がけがちょうどよいほどに大きくなってほしいという、お母さんのねがいがこめられていたのです。

Kintaro

Once upon a time, in a little house at the foot of Ashigara Mountain, there lived a baby boy and his mother. The boy's name was Kintaro, and even as an infant he was unbelievably strong. By the time he could crawl, in fact, he was as powerful as a full-grown man.

Kintaro was his mother's pride and joy, and when he began to walk she sewed him a beautiful, bright red shirt. On the front, embroidered in gold thread, was the character *kin*, for Kintaro. The shirt was much too large for the baby boy, but his mother knew it wouldn't be long before it would fit just right. He was growing bigger and stronger with each passing day.

　ある日、金太郎
は、楽しい仲間と
友だちになること
ができました。そ
れは、山の動物た
ちでした。

　金太郎とお母さんが山の温泉に入っていると、動物た
ちが集まってきました。うさぎ、たぬき、さる。そして、
しかやきつねたちです。

　そのうち、たぬきが一ぴ
き、お湯の中へ入ってきま
した。金太郎とたぬきは湯
をかけあって大はしゃぎ。

　動物たちは、みんな金太
郎が大すきになりました。

　金太郎は、毎日山の中へ入って、動物たちを集めて遊
びます。

「おーい、みんな出ておいでよう。」

「なんだなんだ、あっ、金太郎さんだ。」

「それ行け、やれ行け、えっさっさ。」

　集まった動物たちの先頭に立った金太
郎。山から山へとびまわります。

「向こうのおかまでかけっこだい。」

「えっさ、えっさ、えっさっさ。」

　きょうはかけっこ、あしたはすもう。

Ashigara Mountain was way out in the country, far from any town or village, and Kintaro was a true child of nature. His playground was the forest, and it was easy for him to understand the feelings and languages of all the forest creatures.

One day he and his mother were bathing in the hot spring near their house when a group of animals gathered to watch. Among the animals were a rabbit, a monkey, a squirrel, a deer, a tanuki, and a fox. They wanted to play with Kintaro, but they were too shy to approach him at first. It was the tanuki who finally broke the ice. He jumped into the water to paddle and splash about with the boy, and soon Kintaro and the animals were the best of friends.

Every day from then on, Kintaro would walk up the mountain to meet his animal friends. All day long they'd frolic about in the forest, racing and playing games. Sometimes they held wrestling matches, just for fun, but of course Kintaro always won. The only one who ever beat him was the squirrel. The squirrel scram-

「はっけよい、のこったのこった。」

　動物相手にすもうをとっても、金太郎にかなうものはありません。

「金太郎の勝ち！」

「のこったのこった！　またまた、金太郎の勝ち〜〜っ。」

　そのとき、りすが金太郎の腹がけの中にもぐりこみました。こちょこちょこちょと、りすが動きまわります。

　笑いころげる金太郎。

「りすくんの勝ち〜〜っ。」

　勝ったのは、りすさんだけでした。

　こうして、金太郎はずんずん大きくなり、いつのまにか腹がけもぴったり。

　すもうをしたら、山の動物たちはみんなでかからなければ、とてもかないませんでした。

　みんなでかかってきたって、軽く投げとばしてしまう金太郎でした。

　寒い寒い冬、動物たちは穴にとじこもってふるえていても、金太郎だけはへいきです。

　暑い夏だって、金太郎は元気いっぱい。川に飛びこみ、水遊び。

　あらしの夜、金太郎

bled up inside Kintaro's baggy shirt and tickled him until he fell to the ground, giggling helplessly. The rabbit, who always acted as referee, lifted one of the squirrel's paws and shouted, "The winner!" and everyone laughed.

But by the time Kintaro grew into his oversized shirt, he was so strong that the animals couldn't win even when they all went against him at once. One by one the husky boy would throw them out of the ring as if they weighed nothing at all.

When the cold, cold winter came, the animals would crawl into their holes, shivering, but the freezing weather didn't seem to bother Kintaro at all. Nor did the hot, hot afternoons of midsummer. While everyone else was dozing in the shade, Kintaro would run through the forest or splash about happily in the river. And during the terrifying storms of autumn, he would stand out-

はがんばって家を守ります。ふきとばされそうになる家を、金太郎がしっかとささえます。

そして、金太郎にたいそう力がついたことを知ったお母さんは、ある日、金太郎に大きなまさかりを与えました。

まさかりを持つ金太郎のところへ、いたずらたぬきがきました。

「ねえねえ、金太郎さん、ちょっと持たせて。あ、あ、あっ……。」

たぬきがまさかりを持つと、よろよろっと、ひっくりかえってしまいます。

でも、金太郎は軽々とまさかりをかたにかついで歩きます。

山に秋がきました。ある日、金太郎がまさかりでまき割りをしていると、山の動物たちがそろってやってきました。

「金太郎さん、山へくりをひろいにいきませんか。」

「くりひろい?」

「むこうの山にいっぱいありますよ。」

「よーし、行こうか!」

動物たちは大よろこび。みんなで元気よく、くりひろいにでかけました。

side all night holding down his house so the wind wouldn't blow it away.

When Kintaro was five, his mother gave him a big, heavy axe to carry with him when he went to the forest. Kintaro loved it. He would never use the axe as a weapon, of course—he was such a gentle boy that he even took care not to step on any ants or caterpillars whenever he walked in the forest—but he was glad to be able to help out his mother by bringing home firewood each day.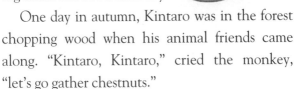

One day in autumn, Kintaro was in the forest chopping wood when his animal friends came along. "Kintaro, Kintaro," cried the monkey, "let's go gather chestnuts."

"Chestnuts?"

"Yes. They're starting to fall from the trees near the top of the mountain."

"All right," said Kintaro. "Let's go!"

And so they started up the mountain, with Kintaro in the lead. They were all in the best of spirits, laughing and chattering, until they came

「あれーっ、橋がないや。」

　このまえのあらしで橋が落ちてしまったのでしょうか。がけにかかっていた橋がありません。

「困ったね……。」

「よーし、この木をたおして橋を作ろう。」

　そばに生えていた大きな木を、金太郎はたおそうとします。

「うーん、うーん。」

　力いっぱいおす金太郎。木は、すこしずつかたむいていきます。

「がんばれ、がんばれ、金太郎さん。」

「ええ〜〜いっ。」

「やったあーっ。」

　金太郎は、とうとう木をたおして橋を作ってしまいました。

　さあ、みんなでそろそろと橋をわたります。金太郎が足をとめました。

「ちょっと待ってね。みんな、虫をふんじゃだめだよ。」

　木の上をはう虫を助けようとしたのです。気はやさしくて力持ち。金太郎は、毛虫一ぴきにもやさしい心を持っていました。

to the Big Gorge and saw that the bridge was down. It had been destroyed in the last storm.

"Oh, no," sighed the fox. "What do we do now?"

"I could cut this down to make a new bridge," said Kintaro, pointing to a tree beside the gorge, "but I don't think it's long enough. I'll have to try to pull it out roots and all."

Well, it was a very big tree, and not even Kintaro, strong as he was, had an easy time of it. But he pulled and groaned and groaned and pulled while the animals cheered him on, and at last he ripped the tree from the ground and threw it across the gorge. It made a perfect bridge.

"Hooray for Kintaro!"

「さあ、もうすぐだぞ。いそげ。」

　橋をわたって、みんなは、どんどん、どんどん山おくへ入っていきました。

　くりのある山は、もうすぐです。

　ところどころに、いまにもはぜて落ちそうなくりの実が見えてきました。

「あっちっちっち……。」

　きょろきょろしていた金太郎は、くりのいがをふんでしまいました。

「あ、くりだ、くりだ。」

「わあい、くりがいっぱい落ちてるぞ。」

　くりはたいへんな豊作でした。形のよいくりがいっぱい落ちています。

　動物たちは大よろこび。金太郎もいっしょうけんめいひろいました。

「よいしょ、よいしょ。」

「いっぱい、あるぞ。」

　ところが、みんなは、むちゅうでくりひろいをしているうちに、だんだん山のおくへおくへと入りこんでしまいました。

　いつのまにか、山いちばんのあばれんぼうのくまがすむという、くま山までできてしまっていたのです。

"Come on, everybody! Let's go get whose chestnuts!"

They crossed the tree-bridge and continued up the mountain, laughing and chattering again, and soon they began to see chestnut trees. Here, however, halfway up the mountain, the chestnuts weren't ripe yet, so they kept on climbing. Kintaro was walking ahead of the rest, gazing up into the branches, when suddenly he cried out.

"Ouch!"

He had stepped right on the prickly shell of a big, ripe chestnut.

"Oh boy, chestnuts!" shouted the fox. "And look at the size of them!"

Kintaro and the animals pranced about picking up all the fallen chestnuts they could find and putting them in their baskets. The higher up the mountain they went, the more chestnuts they found, and before they realized it they had climbed to Bear's Peak, where the biggest, meanest bear on Ashigara Mountain was said to have his lair.

Kintaro was the first to notice. He was poking around for chestnuts when he saw that all the

大きなくりの木のみきに、くまのつめあとがついています。

「あれーっ、なんだか、くまのやつ、いそうだよ。」

　動物たちは、ぶるぶるふるえだしました。

「うお〜〜っ。」

「ひゃーっ、い、いたーっ。」

「ど、どうしよう、金太郎さん、どうしよう。」

　しげみの中から、大きなくまが、のっそりとあらわれたのです。

「ひゃーっ、きたっ。にげよう、き、金太郎さんもにげましょう。」

　動物たちは、ちりぢりににげてしまいました。くまは目のまえです。

「うおーっ。だれじゃ、わしのくり山をあらしとるのは。ゆるさんぞっ。」

　金太郎はへいきな顔です。

「よーし、くまくん、おれが相手だ。さあ、こい。」

「なにをこしゃくな、このこぞう。それっ、行くぞ。ぐわっ、ぐわっ、ぐわっ。」

　くまと金太郎は、がっぷりと組み合いました。

「うーん、こいつはなかなか手ごわいぞ……。」

bark had been scratched away from one of the trees. On the bare trunk were the telltale marks of sharp and powerful claws.

"Uh-oh," he said.

"Grrrr," came a growl from off in the bushes.

All the animals began to quiver with fear. "Kintaro, that sounds like it might be a bear!"

And no sooner had the deer said this than the big bad bear of Bear's Peak came charging out of the brush with a ferocious roar.

"Yikes! Run for your lives! Run, Kintaro!"

The animals scat-tered into the trees, but Kintaro calmly stood his ground.

"Grrr!" growled the bear. "Get off my territory or I'll crush you like a worm!"

"We're not hurting anything, Mr. Bear," said Kintaro politely. "But if you're looking for a fight, I'll be glad to oblige."

"Little squirt! I'll rip you to shreds! Grraaowrr!"

Just as the huge creature reared up, flashing its claws and baring its long, sharp teeth, Kintaro rushed in and clinched it in a powerful bearhug.

「ぐわっ、ぐわっ、ぐわっ。」

「うーん、うーん。」

　草かげで見ていた動物たちは、声をそろえての大声援。

「わーい、金太郎さん、がんばれっ、負けるなよう。」

　とうとう、金太郎は両手でくまを持ちあげました。そしてくまを宙に投げると、落ちてくるくまを両手でしっかりと受けとめたのです。

「やった！　金太郎さんがやった。」

　金太郎の上でくまは、ばたばたとあばれています。

「金太郎さんの勝ちーっ。」

　行司のようにいったのは
うさぎです。金太郎はくま
をはなしてやりました。

　こうして、山いちばんの
あばれんぼうのくまとも仲

"Mmph. Mmph."

"Graowr."

"Mmph. This guy's pretty strong. Mmph."

"Get him, Kintaro. Don't give in!"

All Kintaro's friends were cheering him on, but it looked as if the bear was getting the best of him. Then, suddenly, Kintaro bent back and, with a mighty groan, lifted the great animal up over his head. The bear pawed helplessly at the air.

"The winner and new champion," the rabbit squeaked, "Kintaro–o–o!"

"Hooray!"

Kintaro made the bear promise to be nice before he let him down. And from that day on

よくなった金太郎は、動物たちをひきつれて、お母さんの待つふもとの家へおりてきたのです。

　足柄山の動物と、お母さんの深い愛情に囲まれた金太郎は、それからもすくすくと大きく育っていきました。そして、後に都へ上って、坂田の金時という、とっても強いおさむらいになったということです。

　その坂田の金時の、これはまだ、とてもちっちゃかったころのお話。　　　　　　　　　　　　　　（おわり）

the bear stopped bullying the smaller animals and became one of Kintaro's very best friends.

Soon hunters and woodcutters from miles around were returning to their villages with stories of an unbelievable sight they'd seen on Ashigara Mountain: a little boy in a shirt of red and gold, with a sharp axe over his shoulder, riding bareback on a giant wild bear.

Kintaro had many other exciting adventures, and grew up tall and strong. And it's said that when he became a man, he traveled to Kyoto, where he gained everlasting fame as the brave and invincible samurai Sakata-no-Kintoki.

かぐや姫

むかしむかし、あるところに、竹取りのおじいさんとおばあさんがおりました。

おじいさんは、山から竹を取ってきては、かごやざるを作っておりましたので、人々は竹取りじいさんと呼んでおりました。

ある日のこと、いつものようにおじいさんが竹やぶの中に入っていきますと、どこからかまぶしい光がさして

The Bamboo-Cutter's Tale

ong, long ago, deep in a bamboo forest, there
lived an old man and his wife. Though the
forest was a lovely place, life was rather dreary
and lonely for the old couple, for they were very
poor and had no children of their own to love
and care for.

The old man spent his days outdoors, cutting
bamboo. He used the bamboo to make baskets,
tableware, hats, and other goods which he sold to
the people in town. We no longer know what the
old man's real name was, but in those days everyone simply called him "the bamboo-cutter." And
this is the story of a wondrous thing that happened to him and his wife.

One day the old man was walking through a
dark thicket looking for good, straight bamboo to

きました。なんと、一本の竹が金色に光っているではありませんか。

　ふしぎに思ったおじいさんは、その竹を切ってみることにしました。

　切った竹の光の中には、なんと輝くようなかわいらしい、小さな女の子がすわっておりました。

　おじいさんはその女の子を手にとり、だいじに家につれて帰りました。

「子供のいないわしらに、神さまがおさずけくださったんじゃ。」

「おお、ほんにかわいらしい娘じゃ。」

　おじいさんとおばあさんは、その子にかぐや姫という名をつけて、たいそうかわいがりました。

　かぐや姫を育てるようになってからというもの、おじいさんは、いつも金色に輝く竹を見つけ

cut when he noticed a golden halo of light shining in the darkness. It seemed to come from a single, slender bamboo plant. The old man was astonished. In all his years of cutting bamboo, he'd never run across anything like this, and he decided to cut open the plant to see what made it shine so. He took out his axe and felled the bamboo with one stroke, and you'll never believe what he found.

Inside the hollow stem was tiny baby girl! She was only about three inches high, and she was the cutest thing the old man had ever seen. He lifted the wee girl gently in the palm of his hand and carried her back to this house.

The moment he got home, he called to his wife. "Look what God has sent us," he said. "Our very own daughter!"

"Goodness!" gasped the old woman. "Isn't she beautiful?"

The old man explained the miraculous way in which he'd found the girl, and he and his wife decided upon a name for her: Kaguya-hime, which means "Radiant Princess."

And that wasn't the end of the miracles.

ました。切ってみるとこがねの山です。おかげで、たいそうなお金持ちになっていきました。

　それから三月とたたぬうちに、かぐや姫は、それはそれは美しい娘に成長していきました。その輝くばかりの美しさに、会った人はだれもがうっとりと見とれてしまうほどでした。

　美しいかぐや姫のうわさは、すぐ国じゅうに知れわたり、お金持ちや身分の高い人々が、つぎつぎとかぐや姫をおよめさんにほしいと、もうしこみにやってまいりました。

Almost every day from then on, the old man would come across bamboo plants that glowed with the same golden light. But when he cut these, there were never any little girls inside. Instead, there were piles of gold coins! Before long the old couple were very, very wealthy indeed. And that, of course, allowed them to raise Kaguya-hime in a manner befitting a true princess.

Kaguya-hime grew astonishingly fast, sometimes as much as an inch in a single day. And each day she seemed more radiant and full of life. The old man would watch her racing along with a pinwheel in her hand or chasing dragonflies from flower to flower, and his heart would fill with joy. There's nothing I wouldn't do for that little girl, he often thought.

Of course, she wasn't a little girl for very long. In just three months, Kaguya-hime had become a mature young maiden, so beautiful that one wondered if she could possibly be of this world. Her extraordinary beauty made any man who happened to look upon her fall hopelessly in love.

Word of the bamboo-cutter's lovely daughter spread quickly throughout the land, and rich

けれど、かぐや姫は首を横にふるばかり。

「わたしはどなたのところへも、およめにはまいりません。わたしはずっとおじいさん、おばあさんのそばにいとうございます。いつまでもいつまでも。」

そこでおじいさんは、むりな注文をして結婚のもうしこみをことわろうと考えたのです。

「つぎの品物を持ってこられた方には、かぐや姫をさしあげましょう。」

ともうしわたしました。

「あなたには、光る実のなる金色の枝。つぎの方は、金の毛皮。つぎの方は、光をはなつおうぎ。竜の目玉の首かざり。闇をてらす色紙……。」

young noblemen were soon beating a path to her door to ask for her hand in marriage. But Kaguya-hime refused to see them. "I shall never marry," she told the old man and his wife. "I'll never willingly leave your side."

The old man was secretly gladdened by her words, for he loved Kaguya-hime as much as any father has ever loved his child, and dreaded the thought of losing her. But five of the suitors—five young men of great wealth and standing—were especially persistent. They camped outside the door day and night, pleading for a chance to see Kaguya-hime.

The old man was at a loss as to how to discourage these earnest young noblemen, and as time went by he began to feel sorry for them. At last he decided to have his daughter choose one as her husband. He said to Kaguya-hime:

You shall marry the one who brings you these things. The first is to bring you a golden bough laden with fruit of living amber. The second is to bring an animal skin with fur of purest gold...."

Each of the old man demands was more impossible than the last: a fan that shines like the rising

　どれもこれもむりな注文です。これできっとあきらめるだろうと、おじいさんは考えたのです。

　ところが、なんと男たちは注文の品を持ってきたではありませんか。

　どれもこれも、とても、この世のものとは思えない宝物ばかりです。

　おじいさんは、すっかりこまってしまいました。ところが、かぐや姫の光り輝くほんものの美しさの前には、見せかけの美しさはごまかすことができません。宝物は、みなにせものだったのです。

　やがて、十五夜が近づいてきました。

sun; a necklace made of dragons' eyes; paper that lights up the darkness.

The old man carried this message to the suitors, and the five young men set off immediately, each vowing to return with the gift Kaguya-hime had requested. Easier said than done, thought the old man. He was sure they'd soon abandon all hope of marrying her.

Imagine his surprise when, months later, all five returned with the fabulous treasures demanded of them. The amber fruit, the golden fur, the shining fan, the dragon's-eye necklace, the luminous paper—each was a marvel to behold. But when the gifts were brought before Kaguya-hime, she pronounced them all worthless. And, indeed, her own natural beauty so outshone the glittering baubles that the suitors were forced to admit that they were fakes. The young men left the house dejected and heartbroken, never to see their beloved princess again.

The old man was relieved that the matter was finally settled and that his beautiful daughter would not have to marry and move away. But his happiness was to be short-lived. In the eighth month of that year, a change began to come over

月が輝きを増すにつれて、かぐや姫のひとみには悲しみのかげがただよいはじめました。

おじいさんとおばあさんは、心配になって、かぐや姫に悲しむわけをたずねました。

「かぐや姫や、どうして月を見てそんなに悲しむのじゃ。」

するとかぐや姫は、おばあさんのひざに泣きふしてこういうのです。

「ああ、いつまでもお二人のおそばにいたい。でもわたしは、月へ帰らねばなりません。わたしは月の都のものでございます。」

おじいさんたちはおどろきました。

「なんと、月の都のものじゃと！」

「はい、月の都に住むものは、大人になると、月の都にもどらなくてはならないのです。」

「それは、いつじゃ。」

「はい、八月十五夜の夜に……。」

「十五夜！　じゃ、あしたの夜。そ、そんな！そなたはわしの娘じゃ。だれにもわたすものか。」

Kaguya-hime. Night after night she'd sit and gaze at the moon waxing ever fuller in the sky. And even as the moon grew brighter, the look in Kaguya-hime's eyes grew more wistful and melancholy.

Seeing this, the old man and woman began to worry. "Kaguya-hime, Kaguya-hime, what is it that makes you so sad?" they asked.

Kaguya-hime burst into tears and laid her head on the old woman's lap. "Oh, I wish I could stay with you forever," she sobbed. "But soon I must return."

"Return?" said the old man. "Return where?"

"To the city of the moon, where I was born."

"The city of the moon?"

"Yes. Now that I'm grown, they'll be coming for me."

"What! Who? When?"

"The moon people. On the fifteenth night of this month, when the moon is full."

"But that's tomorrow! I won't hear of it!" cried the old man. "You're our daughter, and no one's going to take you from us."

おじいさんとおばあさんは、かぐや姫をしっかりとだきしめながら、泣きくずれました。

　とうとう十五夜の夜になりました。おじいさんは、できるかぎりの手をつくして、かぐや姫をつれもどしにやってくる、月の使者たちを追いかえそうと、心に決めました。

　おおぜいのさむらいにたのんで、家のまわりの守りをかためます。

　やがて山の上に月が出てきました。さむらいたちは弓に矢をつけ、天にむけます。

　おやしきのいちばん奥の部屋では、おじいさんとおばあさんがかぐや姫を守ります。

　十五夜の月が輝きはじめました。

　身がまえるさむらいたちの上に光の輪が広がります。一人のさむらいが弓を引き、矢をはなちました。

　月に向かって飛ぶ矢。ところが、矢はとちゅうですっときえてしまうのです。ふしぎなほどの月の光に、さむらいたちの目はくらみ、立っていることもできません。

　さむらいたちは、光にうたれ、石のように動かなくなってしまいました。

He and his wife wrapped their arms around the maiden, and all three of them wept. "We'll never let you go, Kaguya-hime," the old man sobbed. "Never!"

The next day, the old man hired a thousand strong samurai to keep the moon people away. Standing shoulder to shoulder, the warriors encircled the house, and even formed a column on the roof. When the moon began to rise over the mountains that evening, they lifted their bows and pointed their arrows at the sky. The old man and woman, meanwhile, sat with Kaguya-hime in the innermost room of the house.

Once the large round moon had risen fully, it cast a brilliant halo of light upon the stolid samurai, who now began to let fly their arrows. But the arrows vanished in midair, and the moonbeams pierced the warriors' armor, paralyzing them where they stood.

　やがて、光の中から天女と天馬がまいおりてきました。
奥の部屋にいたかぐや姫は、すいよせられるように、
月の光の中に立っていきました。

　おじいさんとおばあさんも、どうすることもできません。

「おじいさん、これを……。」

　かぐや姫は、おじいさんの前に命の袋を落としていきました。

「おお、いってしまうのか。か、かぐや姫……。どうか
わたしたちもつれていっておくれ……。」

　おじいさんとおばあさんは、よろよろと、追いかけようとしました。

　その目の前を、かぐや姫ののった天馬が静かに天に登っていきます。そして、みるみるうちに月にすいこまれるように遠ざかっていきました。

Then, from out of that unearthly light, two moon maidens appeared with a winged horse and chariot, descending toward the house. At the same time, the door to the inner room slid open by itself, and Kaguya-hime rose and walked outside, as if drawn by some invisible force. The old man and woman realized now there was nothing they could do to keep her from leaving.

"Kaguya-hime!" they cried, running outside behind her. "If you must go, take us with you."

"I wish I could. You have no idea how much I'll miss you. Please take this as a token of my gratitude for the love you've shown me." So saying, Kaguya-hime dropped a pouch on the ground. "The medicine inside," she said, "will keep you from ever growing older. May you always be healthy and happy. Goodbye!"

Kaguya-hime stepped into the silver chariot, and the winged horse shook its mane and leaped into the sky.

With tears streaming down their faces the old bamboo-cutter and his wife watched the horse, the chariot, and the heavenly maidens disappear in the light of the moon.

Later that night, the old couple stood beside a

おじいさんは、やがて、かぐや姫のくれたいつまでも死なずにすむという、命の薬が入った袋を、火の中にくべてしまいました。

「わしはおまえなしで長生きしても、幸せになんぞなれん。」

　かぐや姫のいないいまとなっては、もう命の袋など持っていたくはなかったのでしょう。おじいさんの思いをたくした炎は、かぐや姫のいる月へ向かって、高く高くのぼっていきました。　　　　　　　　　（おわり）

small fire they'd built outside. The old man was holding the magic pouch that Kaguya-hime had left behind. "So with this medicine we can live forever," he sighed, looking up at the bright full moon. "But without you, Kaguya-hime, how could we ever be happy again? And what good is life without happiness?"

And with these words, he tossed the pouch into the fire.

かちかち山

むかしむかし、あるところに、それはそれは気のいいじいさまとばあさまがすんでおりましたそうな。

こんなじいさまとばあさまに、前山のうさぎもすっかりなついて、毎日のようにあそびにやってきました。

じいさま、ばあさまも、そのうさぎを、自分の子どものように、かわいがっておりました。

いっぽう、うら山のたぬきも、じいさま、ばあさまのところへ、ちょくちょく顔をだしておりました。

ところが、このたぬき、評判のいたずらもの。おまけに、人なみはずれた食いしんぼうときておりましたから、じいさまもばあさまも、すっかり手をやいておりました。

Click-Clack Mountain

Once upon a time there was an old man and his wife who lived in a little farmhouse surrounded by mountains. This kind old couple had a very good friend, a bunny rabbit, who lived on the Mountain in Front. The bunny would come almost every day to visit the old couple. He loved them very, very much, and they in turn treated him just like a child of their own.

Now there was also a tanuki—a kind of badger—who lived on the Mountain in Back and who would often come to the old folks' farm. But his tanuki was a real troublemaker. And he loved eating almost as much as he loved making trouble. He would sneak into the barn, tip over barrels, and nibble on all the fruits and vegetables the old man had worked so hard to grow.

　きょうも、うらの納屋に入りこんで、たるをけたおす
やら、つけものを食いちらすやら、おまけに、じいさま
の笠やくわをひっぱりだすしまつ。
「こらっ、笠を返せ！　くわを返せ！」
　なんとにくらしい。たぬきは、笠とくわを高い屋根の
上にぽんとほうりなげてしまいました。
　さて、そんなある日、じいさまは畑に豆をまこうと、
せっせとくわをふるっておりました。
　そこへ、またもやあらわれたのが、いたずらたぬき。
畑のわきにおいてあった豆の入ったざるをかかえこん
で、豆をむしゃむしゃ食べてしまいました。
「のんきなじいさま、くわ持って、豆もないのに、ほい
さっさ。」
と、ばかにしてはやしたてるのでした。
　あまりいたずらがひどいので、気のいいじいさまもお
こりました。
　とうとうたぬきをつかまえて、なわで、ぐるぐる巻き
にしばりあげてしまったのです。

Once the tanuki even dragged the old man's hat and shovel out-side, just to be mean. When the old man shouted at him—would you believe it?—the tanuki threw the shovel and hat on the roof and scampered away, laughing. The rascal!

Our story begins one day soon after that, when

the old man went out to his field to plant some beans. As he was hoeing the neat rows, along came the mischievous tanuki. The tanuki found the basket with all the beans in it, and when the old man wasn't looking, he dragged it away and ate all the beans up. Then he called out:

"Nyah, nyah, nyah, nyah, nyah,
Stupid old man!
Hoe, hoe, hoe, but where are
your beans?"

Now the old man was very patient and good-tempered, but enough was enough. He ran after the tanuki, caught him by the tail, tied his legs together, and carried him to the house.

「もう、これならいたずらもできめえ。」
と、しばったたぬきをてんじょうからつるして、じいさまは、畑へでていってしまいました。

　家にのこったのは、ばあさまだけです。ずるいたぬきは、なんとかにげだす手はないものかと、考えておりました。

「よーし、なきおとしの手だ。」

　そうおもうと、たぬきはうそなきをして、気のいいばあさまをだましにかかりました。

「ばあさまー。おらは、なんちゅうばちあたりだ。うふん……。せめて死ぬ前に、いままでの罪ほろぼしをして死にてえ。なあ、ばあさま、このなわをほどいてくれ、おら、ばあさまのてつだいがしてえ。」

　たぬきは、なみだを流しながら、話しつづけます。

「ばあさま、おまえさまは年よりだあ、ばあさまの孝行をしてえからよう。」

　聞いていたばあさま、とつぜん首をふりました。

「んにゃ、だまされてなるものか。」

　ばあさまは、そう自分にいい聞かせました。

"Your troublemaking days are over," said the old man angrily. He tied the other end of the rope to the kitchen rafters and left the tanuki hanging upside-down. Then, after telling his wife to keep an eye on the mischief-maker, the old man went out to the field again.

Left alone in the house with the old man's wife, the tanuki began to scheme. "There must be a way out of this," he thought. "I know—I'll make the old woman feel sorry for me!" So the crafty tanuki pretended to weep.

"Good woman!" he sobbed. "What a hope-less sinner I've been." *Sniff, sniff.* "Just once before I die, I'd like to do a good deed. Please untie me, kind lady! Untie me so I can help you with your housework." Tears were streaming down the tanuki's nose and falling on the kitchen floor. "Kind woman, you're not as young as you used to be. It hurts me to see you work so hard. Please let me help you!"

The old woman hesitated, but she shook her head and said, "Uh-unh. You can't fool me."

「なあ、ばあさま、おまえさまは、おらがだますとおも
ってござるじゃろう。死ぬまぎわに、だれがうそなんか
つくもんけえ。てつだいが終えたら、またおとなしくし
ばられる。な、死ぬ前の、たった一つのおねげえだ、な

あ、ばあさま……。」

　ひっしのたぬきのたのみ
に負けて、気のいいばあさ
まは、ついなわをほどいて
しまいました。

「ほれ、しごとてつだえ。」
と、ばあさまがたぬきにき
ねをさしだしました。

「ほんじゃ、つかしてもらおうかい。ばあさまをつくん
じゃい。」

　たぬきは、きねでばあさまをつきとばすと、さっさと
にげだしました。

　そこへ、じいさまが帰ってきました。

「このあくたれたぬきめ！　ばあさまをどうにかしたん
か！」

　じいさまは、あわてて家の中へとびこみました。

「ばあさま！　あああ……。」

　なんと、ばあさま
は、土間にたおれた
まま、息をひきとっ
ておりました。

"I know, I know," said the tanuki. "You think I'm trying to trick you. But would I lie when I'm about to be killed? After I've helped you, you can tie me up again, honest!"

The good old woman was just too softhearted. She hated to see anyone cry. And the tanuki looked so pitiful and harmless hanging upside-down that at last she gave in. She untied him and said, "OK. Take this mallet and pound the rice for me."

"Yes, ma'am!" said the tanuki, taking the heavy wooden mallet. "I'm good at pounding thins. Like old ladies, for instance!" He swung the mallet around  and hit the old woman over the head. She fell to the floor and the tanuki ran outside squealing with glee.

The old man was coming back from the field when he saw the tanuki running away. "Hey, you blasted tanuki! What did you do to Grandma?" he shouted. Imagine how he felt when he found his wife lying dead on the kitchen floor.

"Oh, no!" he cried. "Oh, no!"

　　ほんとにひどいたぬ
きです。
　　ばあさまをなくした
じいさまは、いつまで
もばあさまの墓の前で
ないておりました。

　そんなじいさまを見ていた前山のうさぎは、ばあさま
のかたきは、きっとわたしがうちますと、じいさまをな
ぐさめるのでした。

　それからいく日か、うさぎはたぬきがでてくるのを待
ちました。

　たぬきがやってきました。

「なにしてるだ?」

　たぬきがたずねると、うさぎはかわいい顔でじーっと
たぬきを見つめながら
いいました。

「たきひろいがしたい
んだけど、おら、足が
いたくて……。」

「お、おらにまかせろ、
かついでやるでよ。」

　たぬきは、重いたき

ぎを背負って山をおりはじめました。

　うさぎは、うしろでそっとたきぎに火をつけようと、
火打ち石をならしました。

The next day, the old man dug a grave for his wife and stood before it weeping. Next to him sat the bunny rabbit from the Mountain in Front. The bunny was crying, too. "I'll get that dirty tanuki for this!" he said. "Don't worry, Grandpa. I'll get revenge."

A few days later, the rabbit sat near his home on the Mountain in Front, waiting for the tanuki to pass by. At the rabbit's feet was a bundle of firewood he had gathered.

At last the tanuki came along, chewing on some wild berries. "What'cha doing, Rabbit?" he asked.

The rabbit looked at him and smiled sweetly. "I'm trying to gather firewood. But I hurt my poor little foot...."

"I'll carry your firewood for you—as long as it's downhill," the tanuki said.

"Oh, thank you, Mr. Tanuki!"

The rabbit helped the tanuki strap the bundle of firewood to his back, and they started down the mountain. As they walked along, the rabbit took out a flintstone and began to strike it against a piece of metal. He was trying to set fire to the wood on the tanuki's back.

「おい、うさぎどん、かちかち
いうのは、なにごとだ。」
「かちかち山のかちかち鳥がな
いたんだよ。」
「そうかい、そうかい。」
　そのうち、たきぎがもえだしました。
「おい、うさぎどん、ぼーぼーいうのはなにごとだ。」
「ぼーぼー山のぼーぼー鳥がないたんだよ。」
「そうかい、そうかい。」
　なんにも知らずに歩きつづけるたぬきは、あつさで汗
びっしょりです。
「なんだかあついなあ……、あっ、あちちちっ！　かじ
だあ。」
　かけだしたたぬきは、川にどぼんととびこんで、やっ
と火が消えました。
　背中に大やけどをおったたぬきは、
「あのうさぎを見つけたら、ただじゃおかんぞ！」
と、うさぎをさがしてまわりました。

"Hey, Rabbit, what's that *click-clack* sound I hear?"

"Oh, that's nothing. That's only the Click-Clack Bird from Click-Clack Mountain," the rabbit said, striking the flint.

"Oh," said the tanuki.

At last a spark from the flint caught a dry leaf and the firewood began to burn. Soon the sticks were popping and crackling as the flames grew larger.

"Hey, Rabbit," said the tanuki. "What's that *crackle-crackle* sound I hear?"

"Oh, that's nothing. It's only the Crackle-Crackle Bird from Crackle-Crackle Mountain."

"Oh," said the tanuki. He shrugged and continued walking down the mountain, not knowing that the bundle of wood strapped to his back was aflame.

After a while, the tanuki started to sweat. "Sure is hot," he said. "Hey ... Ow! Yikes! I'm on fire!" The tanuki ran down the mountain screaming until he came to the river and dived in.

Splash! Ssssss ...

The tanuki's back was badly burned. "If I find that rabbit, I'll murder him!" he growled as he climbed out of the river.

すると、みそをすっているうさぎを見つけました。

「このーっ、よくも、おらを！」

「人ちがいしないでよ。あたしは中山のうさぎよ。前山のうさぎじゃないわ。」

「ほんとかや？」

　うさぎは、たぬきをだますと、すました顔でこういいました。

「あんた、やけどしているようね。やけどには、このすりみそがよくきくのよ。」

「おう、これはありがたい。」

　うさぎがすっていたみそには、とうがらしがたっぷり入っていたのです。

　まってましたとばかり、うさぎはたぬきの背中に、べったりとぬってやりました。

「ぎゃおーっ、しみるーっ。」

　背中のやけどにからしみそをすりこまれたたぬきは、もう、ふらふらになって、山をくだりました。

「こんどうさぎのやつを見つけたら、ただじゃおかんぞ！」

Well, he didn't have to look very far. He found the rabbit sitting on a rock nearby, eating *miso* soup. "You've had it, pal!" said the tanuki.

"You must be mistaking me for someone else," said the bunny innocently. "I'm from the Mountain in the Middle. I've never been to the Mountain in Front before."

"Are you sure?"

"Sure I'm sure," said the rabbit. "Say, Mr. Tanuki, you've got a bad burn on your back. You know, this soup is good for burns. Let me rub some of it on you."

"Oh, thank you," said the tanuki.

Now the *miso* soup the rabbit was eating had lots of red pepper in it, and it was very hot. The rabbit dumped the whole bowl on the tanuki's back.

"Yeeeoowww! It burns!" cried the tanuki as he ran stumbling back down the mountain toward the river. He had been fooled again.

"Next time I find that rabbit, I really will kill him," the tanuki grumbled as he sat steaming in the river.

133

そうおもったたぬき
が、またも、うさぎに
であいました。
「このー、よくもひど
いめにあわせたな。」
「人ちがいじゃない？
あたしは、後山のうさ
ぎよ。」

「後山の？　ほんとかあ？」

うさぎは、またも、たぬきをだましにかかりました。
「あんた、魚を食べたくない？」
「魚？　食いてえ！」
「じゃ、舟をつくるのよ。重いたぬきどんは、重いどろ
舟でなきゃだめよ。」

たぬきは、魚を食べたいばかりに、せっせとどろの舟
をつくりはじめました。

舟はできました。うさぎは木の舟、たぬきはどろの舟
で、川にこぎだしました。

Well, it wasn't long before he ran into the rabbit, who was busily building himself a wooden boat a short distance upstream.

"You rat!" snarled the tanuki. "Pulling a dirty trick like that! You can kiss your cottontail good-bye, buddy!"

"You must be mistaking me for someone else," said the rabbit, blinking. "I'm from the Mountain over Yonder."

"The Mountain over Yonder?" said the tanuki suspiciously. "Are you sure?"

"Sure I'm sure," said the bunny. "Say, would you like to eat some fish?"

"Fish? Sure I would!"

"Well, then," said the rabbit, "let's each build a boat. You're big and heavy, Mr. Tanuki, so you'd better make one out of mud."

All the tanuki could think about now was eating fish. He loved fish. So he started making a boat out of mud from the riverbank while the rabbit finished building his own wooden boat. When the two boats were ready, they put them in the river and began paddling.

ところが、どろの舟は水にぬれるとどろりととけてきます。

「うわっ、ど、どうしよう。たすけてくれえっ。」

「ばあさまのかたきだ、おもいしれっ。」

「あっ、やっぱりおまえは前山のうさぎ！」

　とうとうたぬきは、どろの舟といっしょに、ぶくぶくと水にしずんでしまいました。

　うさぎは、ばあさまを殺したたぬきを、ゆるすことができなかったのです。　　　　　　　　　（おわり）

But as soon as the tanuki's mud boat got good and wet, it started to fall apart.

"Oh! Oh!" cried the tanuki. "Help! I can't swim!"

"Remember what you did to Grandma? Well, here's a taste of your own medicine!" shouted the bunny, smashing the tanuki over the head with his paddle.

"Oh, no! You're the rabbit from the Mountain in Front, after all!" the tanuki screamed as he sank into the river with his mud boat.

Glub, glub, glub.

And that's how the rabbit got his revenge on the wicked tanuki.

浦島太郎

　むかしむかし、あるところに、浦島太郎という漁師が住んでおりました。毎日、海へでかけていっては魚をとり、年老いたお母さんと二人で、暮らしておりました。

　その暮らしは、けっして豊かなものではありませんでしたが、浦島太郎は、そんな毎日を送っていても、けっして夢みることをわすれない、心のやさしい若者でありました。いつも、

「お魚になってみたいなあ……。」

なんて、夢みながら、

のんびりこんとつり

糸をたらしているの

でした。

Urashima Taro

Once upon a time, on a little island some- where in Japan, there lived a fisherman named Urashima Taro. Taro's house was on a flower-covered hill overlooking the sea, and every day he'd go down to the shore or out in his boat to fish. Whenever he caught something, he'd bring it back home at the end of the day to give to his kindly old mother.

More often than not, however, Taro caught nothing at all. Not that that ever bothered him, mind you. Taro was a daydreamer, and he was content just to spend his days gazing at the sky, the shoreline, and the beautiful, deep blue sea. It was nothing for him to idle away an entire after- noon staring at the water and imagining what it would be like to be a fish.

こんなふうだから、きょうも、ほかの漁師たちが大きな魚をかかえて浜に上がってくるというのに、太郎のほうは、小さい魚一匹とれませんでした。けれど、浦島太郎は、いっこうに気にかけるようすもなく、ひょっこりひょっこり家路につきました。

　しばらくいくと、悪たれぼうずどもがわいわいさわいでいるのに出会いました。見ると、一匹の子がめをつつきまわしているのです。

　かわいそうに思った浦島太郎は、子どもたちの中にはいっていきました。

「小さなものをいじめちゃいけない。」

　その声に、子どもたちは、くもの子をちらすように逃げていきました。太郎は、あとにのこった子がめをそっと手にのせると、海へはなしてやったのでした。

「気をつけて帰れやー。」

　心のやさしい太郎は、子がめの帰った広い海を、いつまでもいつまでもながめていました。

One evening Urashima Taro was walking along the shore toward home, empty-handed as usual. All the other fishermen had caught as many fish as their boats could hold that day, but Taro hardly seemed to notice. He was smiling to himself, lost in another dream.

He was near his house when he noticed a group of boys standing in a circle, shouting and poking at something with sticks. Taro approached them and saw that they were teasing a baby tortoise.

"Stop that!" he scolded the boys. "You shouldn't pick on creatures that are smaller and weaker than yourselves."

The boys ran away, jeering, and Urashima Taro picked up the baby tortoise and carried it to the water. "There you are, little fellow," he said. "You be careful on your way home, now."

Even after the tortoise had disappeared below the waves, Taro remained on the shore, waving goodbye and gazing at the sea for the longest time.

That's the kind of person Taro was—gentle and good and easygoing. Though he and his mother were anything but wealthy, he was happy

さて、それから、数年がたちました。

あいもかわらず、太郎は、つれてもつれなくても、一日じゅうのんびりと魚をつっておりました。

そしてきょうも、空とぶかもめを見ながら……。

「かもめさんになりたいなあ……。」

なんて、夢をみていると、だれかがつり糸をひっぱるのです。

「うん？」

見ると、大きなかめでした。太郎は、にっこり。それは、太郎が何年か前に助けたかめだったのです。

「太郎さん、その節はほんとうにありがとう。お礼に海の底の美しい御殿に案内しましょう。

その御殿は竜宮といいましてね、海の花にかこまれた、とてもすばらしいところです。さあ、いきましょう。」

かめは浦島太郎を背中にのせると、海の中をどんどん

with his simple, peaceful life. And as he dreamed his days away, the weeks and months and years went by....

One day Taro was in his boat, looking up at the sky and wondering how it would feel to be a seagull, when he felt a great tug on his fishing line. He looked down at the water and saw a large tortoise emerge and swim toward him.

"Urashima Taro," said the tortoise, "I'm the one you saved from those mean little boys a few years back. Do you remember?"

Taro was astonished. He'd never seen a talking tortoise before. "Y—yes," he stammered. "I remember, but—"

"To show my appreciation," the tortoise continued, "I'd like to take you to the Dragon Palace at the bottom of the sea. Wait till you see it! It's the most beautiful place in the world. If you'll just climb onto my back ..."

Taro wouldn't have missed a chance like that for anything. He set down his fishing pole and stepped out of his boat to sit on the tortoise's shell. And no sooner had he done so than they were off.

Down, down, down they went, and the deeper

どんどん泳いでいきました。美しい海底の世界……。そこは、太郎が、いつも夢にえがいていたとおりの、とてもすばらしい世界でした。太郎は、美しい海の世界にすっかりよいしれてしまいました。

　一面、輝くようなさんごの庭。目のさめるような美しさ。その上をふわふわとただよいながら、太郎は、うっとりと夢をみているような、なんともいい気持ちです。

　そのとき、さんごの山が動いたかと思うと、二つに割れて、その中に、きらきら輝く真珠の階段があらわれました。そして、その階段からおりてきたのは、美しいお姫さまでした。竜宮の乙姫さまです。

　その美しさといったら、とてもこの世のものとは思えません。

「どきーん！」

　太郎は、すっかり我を忘れてしまい、ただ、ただ、ぽかんとするばかりです。すると、

乙姫さまが、玉をころがすような美しい声でいいました。

「ようこそ浦島太郎さん、かめを助けてくれてありがとう。

　どうか、ゆっくり遊んでいってください。」

　乙姫さまが、さっとおうぎをひらくと、色とりどりの魚の群がでてきて、太郎をかこみました。乙姫さまのお

the tortoise dived, the more beautiful the scenery became. The bottom of the sea was just as Taro had always imagined, alive with fish of every color, shape, and size, and strange and wonderful flowers that bloomed on rocks and cliffs. Floating weightlessly through this world of marvels, Taro was spellbound by everything he saw.

The tortoise passed through a hole in one of the cliffs, and suddenly they were in a fabulous garden of glittering, glistening coral. They swam through the dazzling display of rainbow colors and came at last to a stairway of shimmering pearls. Taro looked up and his heart began to pound uncontrollably. Coming down the stairs was the most beautiful maiden he'd ever seen.

"Welcome, Urashima Taro," said this lovely vision, with a voice like jewels spilling over glass. "I am Oto-hime, daughter of the Dragon King. The tortoise has told me of your kindness. Please let us entertain you here awhile as a token of our gratitude."

Oto-hime opened her wondrous golden fan and began a delicate, enchanting dance, accompanied by thousands of brightly colored fish

うぎにあわせて舞う、美しい魚の群れ。うず巻く真珠のような水玉。太郎は、もう、大満足。

こうして、竜宮での楽しい毎日がつづいていきました。美しい魚の踊り、舌もとろけるようなごちそう、そして、乙姫さまとのたわむれ。太郎にとっては、ほんとうに夢のような毎日でありました。

しかし、その夢のような毎日も、長くはつづきませんでした。いつしか、太郎の心は、村にのこしてきたおっかさんや、小さな家のことをなつかしく思うようになっていったのです。

日ごとに、元気のなくなっていく太郎をみて、乙姫さまはいいました。

「太郎さん、あなた、帰りたくなったんですね。いつまでもここにいてほしいのですが、しかたありません。」

そして、玉手箱をさしだし、つづけました。

「これをお持ちください。浜へ帰って、もし、とほうに

whose movements filled the water with shining, swirling bubbles. And so began Urashima Taro's stay in the Dragon Palace.

And what a stay it was! Day in and day out Taro lost himself in pleasures such as no man had ever known. Dancing fish, mouthwatering feasts, strolls in the coral garden with the charming, lovely Oto-hime … It was a life beyond his wildest dreams.

Wonderful as it all was, however, it wasn't long before Taro began to miss his village, his little house on the hill, and his kindly old mother. Oto-hime was quick to notice this change in him. One day as he sat on a rock dreaming about the flowers around his house, she approached him and said, "You're anxious to return, aren't you, Urashima Taro? I've grown very fond of you, you know, and I wish you could stay forever. But I understand how you feel."

She left him for a moment and returned with a small lacquered box. "Perhaps the time has come for you to leave. Before you go, however, please accept this box as a reminder of the time we've spent together. If you find yourself confused by anything you see, all you need do is lift the lid.

くれるようなことが
あったら……、その
ときには、この玉手
箱をおあけなさい。」

こうして、太郎は、
かめの背中にのると、
おっかさんの待つなつかしい村へと帰ることになりまし
た。太郎の心は、何日ぶりかで帰る村のことでいっぱい
です。

浜につくと、かめは、太
郎をおろし、また、海へと
帰っていきました。

「かめさん、ありがとう。」

浜には、花が咲き乱れて
いました。その花の中を、
太郎は、わが家めざして走
っていったのでした。

「帰ったぞ、帰ったぞ。」

よろこぶ太郎にだれもこたえてはくれません。あのな
つかしいわが家もありません。おっかさんの姿も見えま
せん。そればかりか、あたりのようすはすっかり変わっ
て……。知っている人も、知っている家もないのです。

さっきの元気はどこへやら。太郎はすっかりとほうに
くれてしまいました。

「とほうにくれるようなことがあったら、この玉手箱を

Remember, though, if you do open the box, you can never return to the Dragon Palace. The choice is yours. Farewell, Urashima Taro."

After these words of parting, Oto-hime called for the tortoise. Taro climbed onto his old friend's back, and together they headed back to the island.

"I hope Mother isn't worried about me," thought Taro. "Oh, I can't wait to get home!"

The tortoise left Taro on the shore outside his village. "Thank you!" Taro shouted as the tortoise swam off again. "Goodbye!" He ran down the beach and up the path toward his house.

"I'm back! I'm home!" he cried happily to everyone he met. Oddly enough, however, he didn't see anyone he recognized. And when he came to the hill where his house should have been, there was nothing but an empty field of wildflowers! In fact, now that he thought about it, everything looked very different indeed. None of the houses nearby seemed familiar, and even the trees were much bigger than they had been when he left.

Taro sat on the ground, bewildered. He was sure that this was his village, yet nothing seemed

おあけなさい。」

太郎の頭に、乙姫さまの声がひびいてきました。

「そうだ！　玉手箱だ。これをあければなにかわかるかもしれない。」

そう思い、太郎は、おそるおそる玉手箱をあけました。すると。あら、ふしぎ、中から白いけむりがもくもく。

そして、若者だった太郎は、たちまちのうちに白いひげのおじいさんになってしまいました。

そうです。太郎が竜宮で楽しい毎日を送っているあいだに、地上では、何百年もたっていたのです。

ぼんやりと、空をふりあおぎながら、太郎は、海の底の美しい世界が夢だったのか、いま、立っているこの世界が夢なのか、よくわからなくなってしまいました。

（おわり）

the same. And where was his house, and his dear old mother?

Suddenly he remembered Oto-hime's parting words. "That's it!" he said to himself. "If I open this box, I'll be able to figure out what's going on." With trembling hands he lifted the lid.

Poof!

A great cloud of white smoke rose from inside the box. Taro coughed and rubbed his eyes. He felt very strange indeed. It was as if all his strength and energy had drained away, as if he weighed nothing at all and was drifting in the wind. And imagine his astonishment when he looked down and saw that he now had a long white beard!

Suddenly everything was clear. While Taro had passed what he thought were only a few days in the Dragon Palace, hundreds of years had gone by on land.

Urashima Taro looked slowly up at the sky. His life with Oto-hime in her palace below the waves—had it all been merely a dream? Or was he dreaming now? The more he thought about it, the less certain he was.

まんが日本昔ばなし
Once Upon a Time in Japan

1997年 3 月10日　第 1 刷発行
1999年 5 月16日　第 7 刷発行

編　者　　川内彩友美

訳　者　　ラルフ・マッカーシー

発行者　　野間佐和子

発行所　　講談社インターナショナル株式会社
　　　　　〒112-8652　東京都文京区音羽1-17-14
　　　　　電話：03-3944-6493（編集部）
　　　　　　　　 03-3944-6492（営業部）

印刷所　　大日本印刷株式会社

製本所　　株式会社 堅省堂

講談社バイリンガル・ブックス

英語で読んでも面白い！

- 楽しく読めて自然に英語が身に付くバイリンガル表記
- 実用から娯楽まで読者の興味に応える多彩なテーマ
- 重要単語、表現法がひと目で分かる段落対応レイアウト

46判変型 (113 x 188 mm) 仮製

1 英語で話す「日本」Q&A / Talking About Japan Q & A

講談社インターナショナル 編 　　　　320ページ　ISBN 4-7700-2026-0

外国の人と話すとき、必ず出てくる話題は「日本」のこと。でも英語力よりも前に困るのは、日本について知らないことがいっぱいという事実です。政治、経済から文化までモヤモヤの知識をスッキリさせてくれる「日本再発見」の書。

2 日米比較 冠婚葬祭のマナー
Do It Right : Japanese & American Social Etiquette

ジェームス・M・バーダマン、倫子・バーダマン 著 　　　192ページ　ISBN 4-7700-2025-2

アメリカでは結婚式や葬式はどのように行われるのか？　お祝いや香典は？……そしてアメリカの人たちも、日本の事情を知りたがります。これだけあればもう困らない。日米冠婚葬祭マニュアル、バイリンガル版。

3 英語で折り紙 / Origami in English

山口 真 著 　　　　　　　　　　　　168ページ　ISBN 4-7700-2027-9

たった一枚の紙から無数の造形が生まれ出る‥‥外国の人たちは、その面白さに目を見張ります。折るとき、英語で説明できるようにバイリンガルにしました。ホームステイ、留学、海外駐在に必携の一冊です。

4 英語で読む日本史 / Japanese History : 11 Experts Reflect on the Past

英文日本大事典 編 　　　　　　　　232ページ　ISBN 4-7700-2024-4

11人の超一流ジャパノロジストたちが英語で書き下ろした日本全史。外国人の目から見た日本史はどういうものか、また日本の歴史事項を英語で何と表現するのか。新しい視点が想像力をかき立てます。

12 英語で話す「日本の心」 和英辞典では引けないキーワード197
Keys to the Japanese Heart and Soul

英文日本大事典 編 328ページ ISBN 4-7700-2082-1

一流のジャパノロジスト53人が解説した「日本の心」を知るためのキーワード集。「わび」「さび」「義理人情」「甘え」「根回し」「談合」「みそぎ」など、日本人特有な「心の動き」を外国人に説明するための強力なツールです。

13 アメリカ日常生活のマナーQ&A / Do As Americans Do

ジェームス・M・バーダマン, 倫子・バーダマン 著 264ページ ISBN 4-7700-2128-3

"How do you do?" に "How do you do?" と答えてはいけないということ、ご存知でしたか？ 日本では当たり前と思われていたことがマナー違反だったのです。旅行で、駐在で、留学でアメリカに行く人必携のマナー集。

14 ニッポン不思議発見！ 日本文化を英語で語る50の名エッセイ集
Discover Japan: Words, Customs and Concepts

日本文化研究所 編 松本道弘 訳 272ページ ISBN 4-7700-2142-9

絶望的な場合ですら、日本人は「そこをなんとか」という言葉を使って、相手に甘えようとする……こんな指摘をうけると、いかに日本人は独特なものの考え方をしているか分かります。あなたも「不思議」を発見してみませんか。

15 英語で日本料理 / 100 Recipes from Japanese Cooking

辻調理師専門学校 畑耕一郎, 近藤一樹 著
272ページ（カラー口絵16ページ） ISBN 4-7700-2079-1

外国の人と親しくなる最高の手段は、日本料理を作ってあげること、そしてその作り方を教えてあげることです。代表的な日本料理100品の作り方を、外国の計量法も入れながら、バイリンガルで分かりやすく説明します。

16 まんが 日本昔ばなし / Once Upon a Time in Japan

川内彩友美 編 ラルフ・マッカーシー 訳 160ページ ISBN 4-7700-2173-9

人気テレビシリーズ「まんが日本昔ばなし」から、「桃太郎」「金太郎」「一寸法師」など、より抜きの名作8話をラルフ・マッカーシーの名訳でお届けします。ホームステイなどでも役に立つ一冊です。

17 イラスト 日本まるごと事典 / Japan at a Glance

インターナショナル・インターンシップ・プログラムス 著 256ページ（2色刷） ISBN 4-7700-2080-5

1000点以上のイラストを使って日本のすべてを紹介——自然、文化、社会はもちろんのこと、折り紙の折り方、着物の着方から、ナベで米を炊く方法や「あっちむいてホイ」の遊び方まで国際交流に必要な知識とノウハウを満載。

18 ビジュアル 英語で読む日本国憲法 / The Constitution of Japan

英文日本大百科事典 編 208ページ ISBN 4-7700-2191-7

難しいと思っていた「日本国憲法」も、英語で読むと不思議とよく分かります。日本国憲法を、59点の写真を使って、バイリンガルで分かりやすく解説しました。条文中に出てくる難解な日本語には、ルビや説明がついています。

19 英語で話す「世界」Q&A / Talking About the World Q & A

講談社インターナショナル 編 　　　　320ページ　ISBN 4-7700-2006-6

今、世界にはいくつの国家があるか、ご存じですか？　対立をはらみながらも、急速に1つの運命共同体になっていく「世界」——外国の人と話すとき知らなければならない「世界」に関する国際人必携の「常識集」です。

20 誤解される日本人　外国人がとまどう41の疑問
The Inscrutable Japanese

メリディアン・リソーシス・アソシエイツ 編　賀川 洋 著 　　　　232ページ　ISBN 4-7700-2129-1

あなたのちょっとした仕草や表情が大きな誤解を招いているかもしれません。「日本人はどんなときに誤解を受けるのか？」そのメカニズムを解説し、「どのように外国人に説明すればよいか」最善の解決策を披露します。

21 英語で話す「アメリカ」Q&A / Talking About the USA Q & A

賀川 洋 著 　　　　312ページ　ISBN 4-7700-2005-8

仕事でも留学でも遊びでも、アメリカ人と交際するとき、知っておくと役に立つ「アメリカ小事典」。アメリカ人の精神と社会システムにポイントをおいた解説により、自然、歴史、政治、文化、そして人をバイリンガルで紹介します。

22 英語で話す「日本の文化」/ Japan as I See It

NHK国際放送局文化プロジェクト 編　ダン・ケニー 訳 　　　　208ページ　ISBN 4-7700-2197-6

金田一春彦、遠藤周作、梅原猛、平川祐弘、西堀栄三郎、鯖田豊之、野村万作、井上靖、小松左京、中根千枝の10人が、日本文化の「謎」を解く。NHKの国際放送で21の言語で放送され、分かりやすいと世界中で大好評。

23 ベスト・オブ・天声人語 / VOX POPULI, VOX DEI

朝日新聞論説委員室 著　朝日イブニングニュース 訳 　　　　288ページ　ISBN 4-7700-2166-6

「天声人語」は「朝日新聞」の名コラムというよりも、日本を代表するコラムです。香港返還、アムラー現象、たまごっち、マザー・テレサの死など、現代を読み解く傑作56編を、社会・世相、政治、スポーツなどのジャンル別に収録しました。

24 英語で話す「仏教」Q & A / Talking About Buddhism Q & A

高田佳人 著　ジェームス・M・バーダマン 訳 　　　　240ページ　ISBN 4-7700-2161-5

四十九日までに7回も法事をするのは、「亡くなった人が7回受ける裁判をこの世から応援するため」だということ、ご存じでしたか？　これだけは知っておきたい「仏教」に関することがらを、やさしい英語で説明できるようにした入門書です。

25 日本を創った100人 / 100 Japanese You Should Know

板坂 元 監修　英文日本大事典 編 　　　　240ページ　ISBN 4-7700-2159-3

混沌と激動を乗り越え築き上げられた現在の日本。その長い歴史の節目節目で大きな役割を果たした歴史上のキーパーソン100人を、超一流のジャパノロジストたちが解説。グローバルな大競争時代を迎えた今、彼らの生き方が大きな指針となります。